G000078832

by P. F. Rawson & J. K. Wright

With contributions by:

I. C. Starmer
F. Whitham
the late J. E. Hemingway

3rd revised edition

Edited by
J. T. Greensmith

ISBN 0-900717-28-9

CONTENTS

PREFACE

Both the Yorkshire coast and our understanding of its geology have evolved since the much-revised second edition of this guide was published in 1992. Major landslips have modified parts of the coast and in some cases obliterated sections, the best-known being the Holbeck Hall landslide at Scarborough in June 1993. Elsewhere, marine erosion has improved the visibility of some sequences. Continuing research has led to some important papers that have significantly improved our understanding of the geological evolution of the area. In addition, excellent revised editions of the BGS maps of Whitby (sheet 35/44) and Scarborough (sheet 54) have now been published at the 1:50,000 scale. For these reasons we decided to update this guide rather than simply reprint it. We have taken the opportunity to add more lithological logs and additional photographs.

Users of this guide are urged to help protect and conserve the exposures described here. A huge number of parties and individuals visit the coast and adjacent moorlands, creating considerable pressure on conservation bodies and landowners. Most of the inland exposures described here are in the North York Moors National Park, while much of the coast is managed by the National Trust or Heritage Coast, who have created pathways along and down the cliffs: please do not stray from the marked routes, and try to avoid disturbing nesting seabirds.

Please bear in mind also that there has been serious overcollecting (especially of fossils) from many of the best known coastal sites. It is rarely necessary to collect fossils *in situ*; excellent specimens can be picked up loose from patches of shingle at many of the localities described - and hammering is forbidden at some of them.

Appropriate Ordnance Survey (OS) and Geological Survey (GS) maps are listed at the beginning of each itinerary. Location maps for individual itineraries are simplified from 1:25,000 OS maps. The whole area is covered topographically in a single sheet by Sheet 36 of Bartholomew's National Map Series at the 1:100,000 scale. The British Geological Survey Tyne - Tees Sheet (1:250,000) also embraces the whole region.

Safety. The Yorkshire coast is reknowned for its rugged beauty. It can also be very dangerous, and there is constant risk of being cut off by the tide. Before following the coastal itineraries consult the local tide tables and unless an access or escape route is immediately adjacent, never start work on a rising tide. The cleanest exposures are often at the cliff foot where there are frequent landslips and an ever-present danger of falling rock; take sensible precautions by keeping away from the cliff foot as far as possible, avoiding areas of recent cliff fall. Safety helmets are essential for work anywhere near the cliff foot, while safety glasses are also necessary when hammering. The shore is often rocky or boulder-strewn, and some of the rocky areas are very slippery - especially where shale scars are covered in an algal slime. Accidents happen, so ensure that someone always knows where you will be visiting, and when.

Acknowledgements. Sadly, Professor John Hemingway, who spent a lifetime researching on the Yorkshire coast and contributed much to earlier editions of this guide, died in 1997. We have retained and updated some of his contributions here. We also acknowledge the assistance of C.R. Ivens and the late D.N. Wright in connection with fieldwork and for some of the photographs. Colin Stuart and Janet Baker (University College London) drew most of the figures, and we are grateful to the Geological Society for allowing us to reproduce figures from our contribution to the Field Guide to the British Jurassic (Rawson & Wright,1996). We thank those readers who made constructive comments on the previous edition and would welcome further suggestions. Finally, we are grateful to a succession of students at UCL who have tested our itineraries during their field training!

The publication of this Guide has been almost totally financially supported by a grant from the Curry Fund of the Geologists' Association. The Petroleum Society of Great Britain also generously donated funds towards the costs of production.

LIST OF FIGURES

LIST OF TABLES

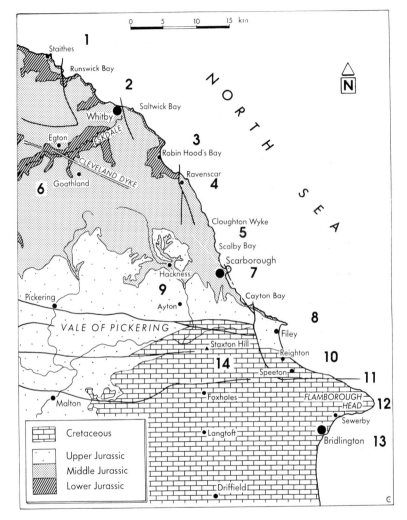

Figure 1. Outline geological map, with itineraries.

INTRODUCTION

The Yorkshire coast provides magnificent exposures of Jurassic and Cretaceous rocks that were deposited in the Cleveland Basin and on the adjacent northern margin of the East Midlands Shelf (Figures 1 & 2). The coastal area is now firmly established as a standard for comparison with both the less well exposed areas inland and also

Introduction

for the offshore North Sea basins. It has attracted the attention of geologists from the earliest days of our science and continues to do so. William Smith visited the area several times in the first two decades of the nineteenth century and recognised almost all the groups of strata that he had previously defined in southern England. Largely through his nephew John Phillips, and particularly after he had settled near Scarborough in 1828, Smith encouraged the publication of descriptions of the fascinating series of rocks he had found. However, local workers were also becoming involved. Young and Bird's *A Geological Survey of the Yorkshire Coast* appeared in 1822. A revised edition was issued in 1828, followed shortly afterwards by John Phillips' *Illustrations of the Geology of Yorkshire; Part 1. - the Yorkshire Coast* (1829). These pioneering works laid a firm though sometimes conflicting foundation for later researchers to build upon.

The structural framework

Towards the end of Triassic (Rhaetian) times the Cleveland Basin and East Midlands Shelf began to develop through differential subsidence, which continued through much of the Jurassic and Cretaceous. Their Mesozoic configuration (Figure 2) may reflect the buried Carboniferous structure (Kent 1980b). The Howardian-Flamborough Fault Belt formed the southern margin of the basin, while its western limit was probably defined by the Pennine High. The northern limit may lie in the Tyne area, as Mesozoic rocks thin in that direction offshore (see maps in Kent, 1980b).

Few faults are known within the basin, except along the coast where several N-S trending ones occur (Figure 2). The best-known is the Peak Fault, whose origin has led to considerable discussion (Itinerary 4). Seismic information offshore now shows that it forms the western boundary to a narrow N-S trending graben, the Peak Trough, which runs obliquely to the coast with the Red Cliff Fault forming its eastern margin (Milsom & Rawson, 1989). Fault movement in the trough probably occurred intermittently from the Triassic through to the Tertiary.

The whole region was gradually uplifted from very late in the Cretaceous through much of the Tertiary (Bray *et al.*, 1992). The uplift was accompanied by inversion of the Cleveland Basin to form the present day E-W trending Cleveland Anticline. The main phase of inversion is assigned either to the Late Cretaceous and Early Tertiary (Kent, 1980a) or to the Tertiary alone (Hemingway & Riddler, 1982). This inversion mainly reflects compression from the south (Alpine movements). The axes of several subsidiary domes and troughs are aligned obliquely to the main axis (Figure 3). The Lockton and Eskdale domes have yielded gas, the latter in commercial quantities. The most spectacularly exposed of these minor fold structures is the Robin Hood's Bay dome on the coast southeast of Whitby (Itineraries 3 and 4; Figure 17).

The northern part of the East Midlands Shelf forms the Market Weighton High. This regionally important structure was originally described as an anticline, but is

Introduction

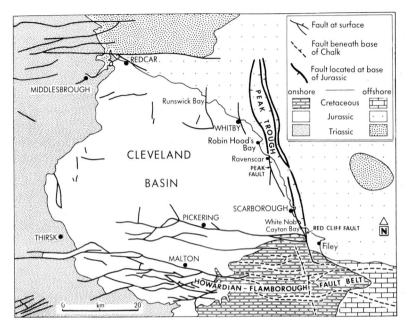

Figure 2. The structural framework. (After Kirby & Swallow, 1987; Milsom & Rawson, 1989; BGS 1:50,000 Sheet 54 Scarborough, 1998).

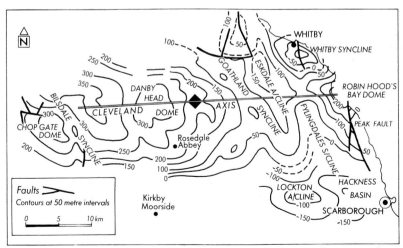

Figure 3. Structural inversion of the Cleveland Basin. Based on contours drawn on the top surface of the Dogger Formation (modified from Kent, 1980b, fig. 24, and Hemingway & Riddler, 1982).

Introduction

now regarded as a rigid E-W orientated unfolded block which remained buoyant throughout Jurassic and Cretaceous times (supported by a deeply buried granite: Donato, 1993) while the Cleveland Basin to the north was subsiding rapidly. The high is essentially a hinge between the shelf and the basin, the main line of inflection being the Howardian - Flamborough Fault Belt. The history of faulting in this belt is still poorly known but probably started during the Carboniferous, when it might have been contiguous with the Craven Fault Belt some 140 km to the west.

STAGE / SUBSTAGE	AMMONITE ZONE	LITHOSTRATIGRAPHICAL DIVISION		
182 Ma	Dumortieria levesquei	Blea Wyke Sandstone Formation	Yellow Sandstone Mbr	9 m
			Grey Sandstone Mbr	9 m
TOARCIAN	Grammoceras thouarsense	Whitby Mudstone Formation	Fox Cliff Siltstone Mbr	11 m
			Peak Mudstone Mbr	13 m
	Haugia variabilis		Alum Shale Mbr	37 m
	Hildoceras bifrons			
	Harpoceras falciferum		Mulgrave Shale Mbr	32 m
	Dactylioceras tenuicostatum		Grey Shale Mbr	14 m
UPPER PLIENSBACHIAN (DOMERIAN)	Pleuroceras spinatum	Cleveland Ironstone Formation	Kettleness Mbr	10 m
	Amaltheus margaritatus		Penny Nab Mbr	19 m
LOWER PLIENSBACHIAN (CARIXIAN)	Prodactylioceras davoei	Staithes Sandstone Formation		25 m
	Tragophylloceras ibex	Redcar Mudstone Formation	"Ironstone Shales"	64 m
	Uptonia jamesoni		"Pyritous Shales"	27 m
UPPER SINEMURIAN	Echioceras raricostatum		"Siliceous Shales"	38 m
	Oxynoticeras oxynotum			
	Asteroceras obtusum			
LOWER SINEMURIAN	Caenesites turneri		"Calcareous Shales"	127 m
	Arnioceras semicostatum			
	Arietites bucklandi			
	Schlotheimia angulata			
HETTANGIAN	Alsatites liasicus			
204 Ma	Psiloceras planorbis			

Table 1. Subdivision of the Lower Jurassic (Hettangian-Toarcian) sequence. The age is indicated in millions of years (Ma).

NOTE: The Mulgrave Shale Member was proposed in the previous edition of this guide (Rawson & Wright, 1992) as a replacement name for the Jet Rock Member of Powell (1984). This was to avoid confusion with the "Jet Rock sensu stricto", the lowest of three informal divisions commonly used within the member (the other two being the Bituminous Shales and the Ovatum Band). The name is derived from Powell's reference section at Port Mulgrave,

Introduction

The Jurassic rocks of the Howardian Hills are intensively disturbed by a series of E-W faults, which pass eastwards beneath the Chalk (Kirby & Swallow, 1987). They probably originated as Jurassic growth faults and were intermittently active during the Late Jurassic and Early Cretaceous (Late Cimmerian movements). Thus, at times, a submarine or subaerial fault scarp probably formed the northern boundary of the Market Weighton High. Further reactivation occurred after deposition of the Chalk, indicated by E-W trending faults and 'shatter belts' in the Chalk (Itineraries 12, 14). This movement was another local response to more widespread events, reflecting both the Laramide (end-Cretaceous to Paleocene) movements and the Alpine orogeny (Oligocene-Miocene), and embraced both tensional and compressional phases (Starmer, 1995a; Itineraries 12, 14).

For much of Jurassic time the Market Weighton High probably formed an area of shallow water deposition, though those post-Liassic sediments which originally extended over it were removed by pre-Albian erosion (see Tables 1-4 for stage/age terms). From Mid Volgian to Early Albian times it appears to have been emergent, forming a barrier between the Cleveland Basin and the shelf to the south, until it was finally submerged again by the Mid Albian marine transgression.

Palaeogeography and environments

Sea-level rise in latest Triassic to earliest Jurassic times established a marine regime over the region, which was marginal to the Southern North Sea Basin (Figure 4a). Early Jurassic shorelines generally lay some distance from present outcrops and the sequence consists predominantly of offshore argillaceous sediments, though shallow-water facies of varied origins also occur. The Lower Jurassic sediments are placed in the Lias Group, the nomenclature of which has been revised by Knox (1984), Powell (1984) and Howard (1985); five formations are recognised (Table 1), while many of the long-established smaller, essentially lithological, subdivisions have been retained and formalised as members.

The Siliceous Shales (Redcar Mudstone Formation) are the lowest unit to be seen in detail in the itineraries to be described in this guide. They consist of silty shales with thin harder siltstones, the latter forming the harder ledges picked out by the sea in the intertidal zone at Robin Hood's Bay (Itinerary 3). Sellwood (1970, 1972) suggested that each siltstone band formed the top of a small-scale (1-4 m) coarsening-upward cycle, which he attributed to variation in sea-level. However, the careful logging of the sequence by Hesselbo and Jenkyns (1996) shows that there are upwards of 70 of these sandy incursions varying considerably in their thickness and in the degree to which scouring was involved in their deposition. The suggestion of Buchem and McCave (1989) that the whole sequence was laid down in a fairly shallow marine shelf subject to periodic storm conditions, and that the sandy beds represent proximal to distal storm beds deposited by storms of widely varying intensity, is gaining acceptance today.

Introduction

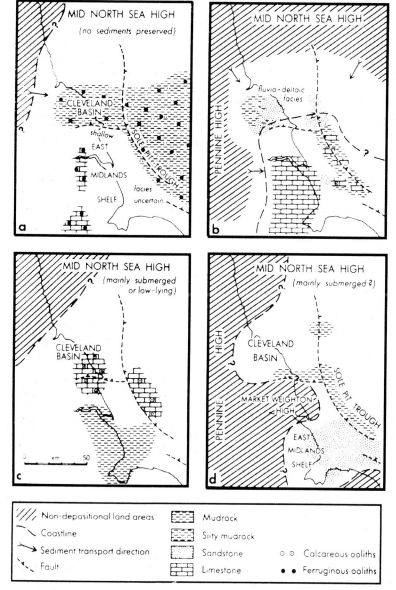

Figure 4. The palaeogeographical setting. (a) Early Jurassic (b) Mid Jurassic (c) Late Jurassic (d) Early Cretaceous

Introduction

This long interval of shallow marine sedimentation was terminated abruptly by the earliest Pliensbachian sea-level rise which restored deeper water shale sedimentation to the basin. But later Pliensbachian times saw a further shallowing of the sea and argillaceous sands and silts were deposited to form the Staithes Formation (Itinerary 1). Storm-influenced sedimentation again played an important role at this time. Much of the sediment was derived from a Pennine landmass to the northwest. A shoreline in that direction is also indicated by the overlying Cleveland Formation. This consists of a nearshore sequence in Cleveland dominated by oolitic ironstones, passing to the southeast into a more argillaceous, deeper water succession composed of a series of minor coarsening-upward cycles on a similar scale to those of the Siliceous Shales. Each cycle is capped by an ironstone; the iron was presumably leached from a low-lying, subtropical, well-vegetated landmass.

The Toarcian saw important changes in the pattern of sedimentation in basins across Britain, reflecting a global rise in sea-level. This ushered in a new phase of mudrock sedimentation (Whitby Mudstone Formation). The lowest unit, the Grey Shales Member, contains a rather sparse, normal marine fauna dominated by ammonites. It has a sharp, though conformable, basal contact with the Cleveland Ironstone Formation.

The Mulgrave Shale Member is a finely-laminated mudrock that shows evidence of oxygen depletion in the bottom waters. There is a very restricted bottom-living fauna (Morris, 1979) though the specialised, opportunistic bivalve *Pseudomytiloides dubius* is common. In contrast, there is quite a diverse fauna of free-swimming animals (ammonites, fish, reptiles, etc.). The main water mass must therefore have been well oxygenated while the sea floor was generally oxygen-deficient. The member is the local representative of a much more widespread 'anoxic event', and such shales were deposited over much of Europe (Posidonienschiefer, Schistes Carton, etc.). They form a source rock for oil in North Germany, the Netherlands and the Paris Basin, and when freshly broken the Yorkshire sediments smell strongly of oil. The lower part of the Mulgrave Shale Member ('Jet Rock' *sensu stricto*) is more finely and persistently laminated than the higher part ('Bituminous Shales') and represents peak anoxic conditions (Pye & Krinsley, 1986). Jet itself occurs as very thin, elongate coal-like seams, which are flattened, drifted logs of wood allied to the modern auracarians.

The overlying Alum Shale Member marks a return to 'normal' marine mudstone sedimentation, with some bottom-living organisms including abundant examples of the mud-burrowing bivalve *Dacryomya ovum*. Rare trace fossils occur, including *Thalassinoides*.

Higher Toarcian rocks are preserved only in small pre-Dogger (Mid Jurassic) synclines and are best exposed along the coast immediately to the southeast of the Peak Fault. Here, the shallower water sediments above the Alum Shale Member form a sequence of three fining-upwards cycles (the lowest forming the Peak

STAGE	LITHOSTRATIGRAPHICAL DIVISION		
BATHONIAN 160 Ma	Scalby Formation 60 m		Long Nab Member
UPPER BAJOCIAN ?			Moor Grit Member
LOWER BAJOCIAN	Ravenscar Group	Scarborough Formation (m) 30 m	
		Cloughton Formation 85 m	Gristhorpe Member
			Lebberston Member (m) 9 m
			Sycarham Member
?		Eller Beck Formation (m) 8 m	
AALENIAN		Saltwick Formation 57 m	
182 ma		Dogger Formation (m) 12 m	

Table 2. Subdivision of the Middle Jurassic (Aalenian-Bathonian) sequence.

Mudstone Member and the other two the Fox Cliff Member) overlain by two coarsening-upwards cycles (Grey Sandstone and Yellow Sandstone Members). Individual cycles vary between 9 and 12.6 m maximum thickness (Knox, 1984).

These phases of Late Toarcian shallowing may reflect successive early pulses in regional uplift and the creation of an extensive landmass over much of the central and northern North Sea. This culminated at the beginning of the Aalenian (Mid Jurassic). There then followed a regional sea-level fall and a radical change in palaeogeography (Figure 4b). Deltaic and fluviatile sediments emanating from the newly uplifted land area poured into the Cleveland Basin, in contrast to central and southern England which were covered by a warm, shallow shelf sea. At times seawater spilled into the basin from the south or east, so intercalating thin marine beds in the fluviodeltaic sequence.

The shallow marine Dogger Formation, which generally rests unconformably on Lower Toarcian sediments, is a complex unit, ferruginous throughout. Over much of the basin the formation is sandy, and in the present day coastal area is predominantly a tough, sideritic sandstone with a pebbly base. Towards the northwest, chamosite oolites and bioclastic limestones appear and a coastline probably lay to the north and west (Hemingway, 1974).

The depositional environment of the non-marine beds of the overlying Ravenscar Group (Table 2) has caused much discussion. The initial estuarine hypothesis of Fox-Strangways (1892) has long been superseded and the debate now centres on deltaic versus alluvial plain environments. The group shows features characteristic of both. Coarsening-upwards cycles of bioturbated, laminated, intertidal siltstones

Introduction

with crevasse splay sheet sandstones, succeeded by rapidly filled distributory channels with slumps and water escape structures, suggest a deltaic origin. Meandering streams, superbly seen in the meander belt at Scalby Bay (Itinerary 5), flood plains with desiccation cracks and footprint trails, lakes with beds of the bivalve *Unio*, marsh deposits, fossil soils with rootlet beds and the extensive development of sphaerosiderite all point to an alluvial origin.

The overall evidence suggests that following the marine intervals of the Dogger Formation, Eller Beck Formation, Lebberston Member and Scarborough Formation, there was a rapid development of small prograding deltas, ultimately coalescing into a large alluvial plain; there is no evidence for a large single river system feeding into a large delta. The plain was always close to sea-level and susceptible to marine influence. The Scalby Formation shows the least marine influence, with a substantial thickness of the middle and upper Long Nab Member showing no sign whatsoever of marine microflora or of marine bioturbation.

While the marine incursion represented by the Lebberston Member probably came from the shelf to the south, the Eller Beck and Scarborough Formation transgressions were probably from the east (Knox, 1973; Parsons, 1977). The Scarborough Formation is firmly dated as mid Bajocian, while the overlying Moor Grit and basal Long Nab Members of the Scalby Formation have yielded very sparse dinoflagellate floras of latest Bajocian to Bathonian age. Dinoflagellates from the upper Long Nab Member at Newtondale indicate a Bathonian age (Riding & Wright, 1989). The evidence for a major break in the succession either beneath or above the Scalby Formation (Nami & Leeder, 1978) appears slim.

During the Early Callovian the sea again transgressed into the Cleveland Basin from the east (Wright, 1977), the Cornbrash Limestone Formation resting on a bored erosion surface cut in Scalby Formation silts. Sea-levels continued to rise (following a global trend) to reach a local peak at about the Oxfordian/ Kimmeridgian boundary. Since Upper Jurassic sediments are not preserved over most of the structural highs it is difficult to assess the distribution of land and sea, but facies patterns suggest that eventually most of the Mid North Sea High was flooded while the Pennine and Market Weighton Highs were at least partially submerged (Figure 4c).

Callovian to Kimmeridgian sediments of the Cleveland Basin show significant facies differences to those on the East Midlands Shelf, though some of the changes took place away from the vicinity of the Market Weighton High and do not necessarily reflect instability of the High. Both the Kellaways Formation sands and much of the Oxford Clay Formation of the shelf are replaced north of the Vale of Pickering by a single sandy unit, the Osgodby Formation. This represents three phases of sedimentation separated by periods of erosion. For the first two phases the predominant source of sediment was to the northwest, though there is evidence of minor input from the east. Sediment incursion from these sources slowed down by the third phase, when sands of the preceding two phases were locally reworked.

Introduction

Wright (1978) has suggested that it was during the second phase (*coronatum* Zone) that the Market Weighton High was submerged to allow the Oxford Clay seas to spread clay northwards into the Vale of Pickering. By the beginning of the Oxfordian finer-grained sediments spread over the whole area to deposit a silty facies of the Oxford Clay Formation at least as far north as Scarborough.

Oxford Clay sedimentation did not last for long before the basin began to fill up and calcareous sandstones (grits) and limestones, including oolites and coral reefs, of the Corallian facies accumulated. These are equivalent to the highest Oxford Clay and much of the Ampthill Clay Formations of the East Midlands Shelf and indicate a second phase of inversion of basin and shelf. The Corallian facies in general indicate a warm, very shallow, well oxygenated sea in which carbonate banks and coral reefs developed. Fine-grained (micritic) limestones accumulated in the slightly deeper, backreef lagoons. The Lower Calcareous Grit, Coralline Oolite and Upper Calcareous Grit Formations constitute the Corallian Group (Table 3) but the rapid lateral and vertical changes within them, especially in the Coralline Oolite Formation, have resulted in a plethora of names for local members (summarised in Wright, 1972, 1983).

The Lower Calcareous Grit Formation is predominantly a *Rhaxella* (sponge) spiculite containing a small proportion of fine quartz sand, which was probably derived from the northern margin of the Market Weighton High (Wright, 1983). The siliceous spicules are readily dissolved and are the source of diagenetic cement which is often concentrated into chert nodules and bands. The settled, quiet conditions necessary for prolific growth of sponges seem to have suited ammonites very well, and the calcareous concretions of this formation yield in abundance some of the best preserved examples found in Britain. Increasing wave energy, warm, shallow shelf seas and minimal clastic input resulted in the deposition of substantial thicknesses of oolitic and shelly limestones. William Smith's term Coralline Oolite (Formation) is still used for these beds, corals occuring at many horizons. At three horizons near the base, middle and top of the formation the water cleared sufficiently for large patch reefs to develop. Some fine-grained sandstones occur too, the thickest being the Middle Calcareous Grit Member. This unit was derived from the north or northwest, whereas the Birdsall Calcareous Grit Member (Itinerary 8) was derived from the south. Progressive uplift of the source areas brought an end to the reefs as red, lateritic clay was washed in. The clay is succeeded by siltstones, fine-grained sandstones and silicified *Rhaxella* spiculites of the Upper Calcareous Grit Formation.

In Late Oxfordian times the Ampthill Clay facies spread northwards beyond Market Weighton to at least the Vale of Pickering. Clay sedimentation extended over the whole area by the beginning of the Kimmeridgian - a local reflection of a sea-level rise that led to a blanket of clay being deposited over much of the North Sea area from then on to the end of Early Cretaceous times. The Kimmeridge Clay Formation is poorly exposed (Itinerary 10) but has been penetrated by several boreholes in the Vale of Pickering (Herbin *et al.*, 1991). Clay sedimentation

Introduction

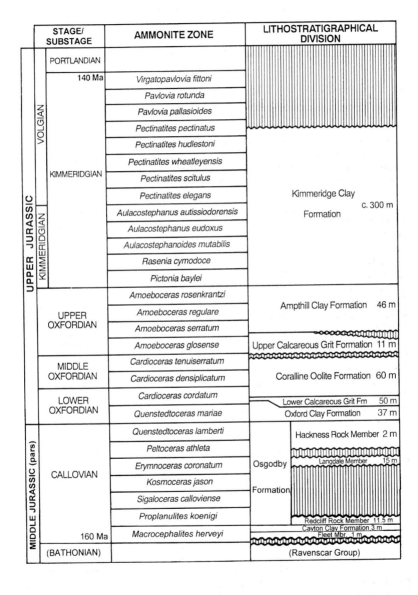

	STAGE/ SUBSTAGE		AMMONITE ZONE	LITHOSTRATIGRAPHICAL DIVISION	
UPPER JURASSIC	VOLGIAN	PORTLANDIAN			
		140 Ma	*Virgatopavlovia fittoni*	Kimmeridge Clay Formation c. 300 m	
			Pavlovia rotunda		
			Pavlovia pallasioides		
			Pectinatites pectinatus		
			Pectinatites hudlestoni		
			Pectinatites wheatleyensis		
	KIMMERIDGIAN	KIMMERIDGIAN	*Pectinatites scitulus*		
			Pectinatites elegans		
			Aulacostephanus autissiodorensis		
			Aulacostephanus eudoxus		
			Aulacostephanoides mutabilis		
			Rasenia cymodoce		
			Pictonia baylei		
	UPPER OXFORDIAN		*Amoeboceras rosenkrantzi*	Ampthill Clay Formation 46 m	
			Amoeboceras regulare		
			Amoeboceras serratum		
			Amoeboceras glosense	Upper Calcareous Grit Formation 11 m	
	MIDDLE OXFORDIAN		*Cardioceras tenuiserratum*	Coralline Oolite Formation 60 m	
			Cardioceras densiplicatum		
	LOWER OXFORDIAN		*Cardioceras cordatum*	Lower Calcareous Grit Fm 50 m	
			Quenstedtoceras mariae	Oxford Clay Formation 37 m	
MIDDLE JURASSIC (pars)	CALLOVIAN		*Quenstedtoceras lamberti*	Hackness Rock Member 2 m	
			Peltoceras athleta	Osgodby Formation	
			Erymnoceras coronatum	Langdale Member 15 m	
			Kosmoceras jason		
			Sigaloceras calloviense		
			Proplanulites koenigi	Redcliff Rock Member 11.5 m	
		160 Ma	*Macrocephalites herveyi*	Cayton Clay Formation 3 m / Fleet Mbr. 1 m	
	(BATHONIAN)			(Ravenscar Group)	

Table 3. Subdivision of the Middle to Upper Jurassic (Callovian-Volgian) sequence.

Introduction

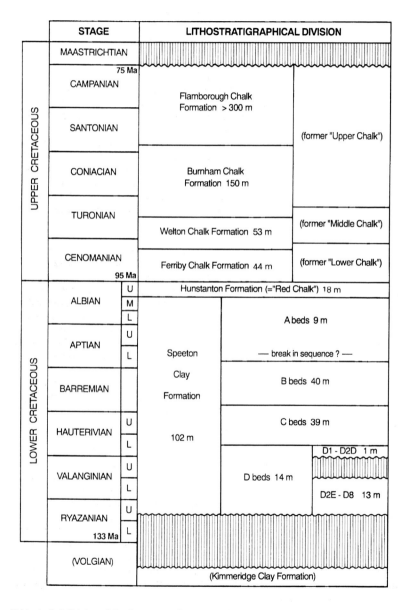

STAGE			LITHOSTRATIGRAPHICAL DIVISION		
	MAASTRICHTIAN				
UPPER CRETACEOUS	75 Ma				
	CAMPANIAN		Flamborough Chalk Formation > 300 m		(former "Upper Chalk")
	SANTONIAN				
	CONIACIAN		Burnham Chalk Formation 150 m		
	TURONIAN		Welton Chalk Formation 53 m		(former "Middle Chalk")
	CENOMANIAN		Ferriby Chalk Formation 44 m		(former "Lower Chalk")
	95 Ma				
LOWER CRETACEOUS	ALBIAN	U	Hunstanton Formation (="Red Chalk") 18 m		
		M	Speeton Clay Formation 102 m	A beds 9 m	
		L			
	APTIAN	U		— break in sequence ? —	
		L		B beds 40 m	
	BARREMIAN				
	HAUTERIVIAN	U		C beds 39 m	
		L			D1 - D2D 1 m
	VALANGINIAN	U		D beds 14 m	
		L			D2E - D8 13 m
	RYAZANIAN	U			
	133 Ma	L			
	(VOLGIAN)		(Kimmeridge Clay Formation)		

Table 4. Subdivision of the Cretaceous (Ryazanian-Campanian) sequence.

continued until early *pectinatus* Zone or, locally, *pallasioides* Zone times. It then apparently ceased for about 9 million years (during which interval the sea probably remained over the area; Rawson & Riley, 1982) before commencing again with deposition of the Lower Cretaceous Speeton Clay Formation (Table 4).

The Speeton Formation accumulated to the north of an emergent Market Weighton High (Figure 4d) which separated it from the more varied facies of the East Midlands Shelf. It crops out as faulted inliers in the Vale of Pickering and in a strip along the Wolds escarpment to reach the coast south of Filey, where it is well exposed at the type section at Speeton (Itinerary 10). There the clays are only about 100 m thick, but they provide a unique sequence through the British marine Lower Cretaceous, the lower (and better preserved) part of the section correlating with the non-marine Wealden facies of southern England. The faunal and floral successions provide a standard for comparison with the North Sea and North German successions. Thin volcanogenic mudstones at several levels (Knox, 1991) reflect the activity of distant volcanoes, possibly in the Dutch sector of the southern North Sea.

The Speeton Formation passes up into a thin red limestone - the Hunstanton Formation ('Red Chalk') - deposited as rising sea-levels flooded the Market Weighton High again. As clastic input diminished a pure white limestone, the Chalk, began to accumulate, composed of calcareous algal plates (coccoliths) deposited as copepod faecal pellets in a clear warm sea that eventually extended over almost the whole of Britain and adjacent areas. The Chalk Group forms the arcuate hills of the Wolds, reaching the sea at Flamborough Head to form a magnificent sweep of cliffs about 17 km long. The lowest beds of the Chalk Group can be seen at Speeton (Itinerary 10), but the overlying sequence in Buckton and Bempton cliffs is inaccessible. However, the famous contortion zone at Staple Nook (Starmer, 1995b) is readily seen from pleasure boats and together with the structure in Selwicks Bay (Itinerary 11) forms part of the Howardian-Flamborough Fault Belt. In the Flamborough region the beds are accessible again (Itineraries 11 to 13).

A major revision of the stratigraphy of the Chalk of the northern province (Yorkshire to North Norfolk) was published by Wood and Smith (1978). The former division into Lower, Middle and Upper Chalk was unsatisfactory and the long established fossil zones were very vaguely defined. In the modern lithostratigraphy, the Chalk Group is divided into four formations (Table 4). Recognition of the lateral continuity of flint and marl bands has resulted in numerous named marker horizons in the lowest three units. Some of the marl bands in the Welton and Burnham Formations are now believed to be of volcanogenic origin (Wray & Wood, 1998). The Flamborough Formation has now been subdivided too (Whitham, 1993). Thus there is a firm framework against which fossil occurrences can be calibrated (Whitham, 1991, 1993). Much of the sequence is demonstrated in Itineraries 10-14.

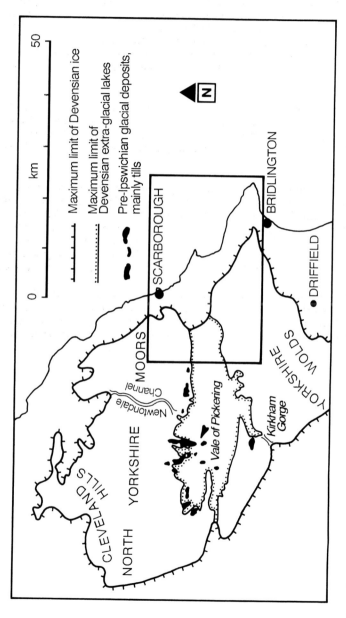

Figure 5. Palaeogeography of the area during the last (Devensian) glaciation. (Modified from Kent 1980b, fig. 27). The rectangle indicates the area shown in detail in Figure 47.

Introduction

No Tertiary sediments are known from the area, although sands and clays preserved in solution hollows in the Chalk of the Wolds were considered by Versey (1939) to be of pre-glacial (i.e. Tertiary) age. The burial history of the Cleveland Basin also indicates that some Lower Tertiary sediments may have been deposited, then removed during basin inversion later in the Tertiary. Hemingway and Riddler (1982) deduced that as much as 1-1.25 km of Tertiary sediments have been removed.

Tertiary igneous activity is represented by the Cleveland Dyke, a tholeiitic basalt intrusion peripheral to a volcanic province centred on the western Scottish island of Mull. The dyke does not reach the coast but is visible on the North Yorkshire Moors (Itinerary 6). It has been radiometrically dated to 58.4 ± 1.1 Ma (i.e. Eocene) (Kent, 1980b, p. 107).

During the Pleistocene ice age the area was glaciated at least twice, though only a few relics remain of deposits pre-dating the last (Devensian) glaciation. During the Devensian much of the higher land probably remained ice-free, but glaciers passed down the Vale of York and also abutted against the northern flanks of the North Yorkshire Moors and the coast (Figure 5). Ice also infilled the pre-glacial bays. Meltwater flowed southward into the Vale of Pickering to form a large glacial lake (Figure 48 and Itineraries 6, 14). The main deposits left behind are the tills (which fill the core of each bay), sand and gravel moraines and lacustrine varved clays. The tills (boulder clays) are composite sheets containing erratic pebbles and boulders derived from at least three distant sources - Scandinavia, Scotland and the Lake District - as well as more local material. It is the subsequent erosion of this material that provides such a rich and fascinating suite of pebbles on our beaches - including the carnelians and agates so popular with collectors.

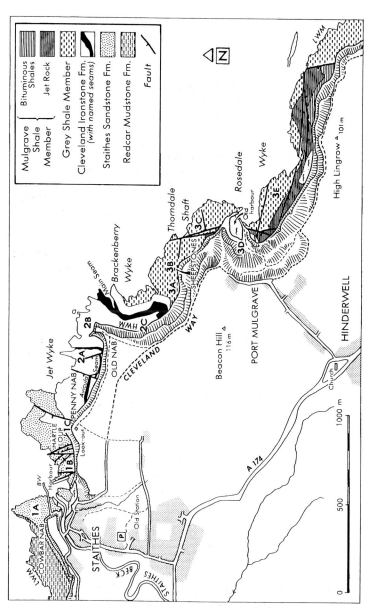

Figure 6. Map of the Staithes to Rosedale Wyke shore (Itinerary 1). (Based mainly on Howarth, 1955, 1962, 1973).

Staithes to Port Mulgrave

ITINERARY 1

Staithes to Port Mulgrave

P. F. Rawson

OS   1:25,000 Outdoor Leisure Map Sheet 27
            1:50,000 Landranger 94 Whitby
GS   1:50,000 Sheet 34 Guisborough

The 3 km stretch of coastline between Staithes and Port Mulgrave provides a magnificent series of exposures of the Lower Jurassic Staithes Sandstone, Cleveland Ironstone and lower Whitby Mudstone Formations. The rugged splendour of this coastline has been much modified by man; the former working of ironstone, alum shale and jet in the area has left extensive evidence, some of which is mentioned below. Now, the skyline to the west of Staithes is dominated by the Boulby potash mine.

The route is mainly over a rocky wave-cut platform and **a falling tide is essential** as the rising sea reaches the foot of the cliff in places by about mid-tide.

Locality 1. Staithes to Penny Nab (Staithes Sandstone Formation).

Staithes is a picturesque fishing village which retains much of its original character - though many of the cottages are now second homes. From the village car park (Figure 6) walk down the main road, noting to the left the 30 m deep gorge cut through the Staithes Sandstone Formation by the postglacial Staithes Beck. Continue through the older part of the village to the harbour wall (NZ 784188), where the Staithes Sandstone Formation (28.6 m thick) can be seen in the cliffs on both sides of the harbour. Howarth (1955) showed that the lower part of the formation belongs to the *davoei* Zone (12.6 m thick according to Howard, 1985) and the upper part to the *margaritatus* Zone (16 m thick). It consists of shallow marine sandstones and siltstones with clearly displayed sedimentary structures. The thicker bedded units are often cross-bedded; they include excellent examples of hummocky cross-stratification, which is believed to have formed through the reworking of shallow sands by oscillating storm waves. Thinner-bedded units consist of sheets of fine sandstone fining-upwards to mudstone, the base of individual sheets being erosive. They show delicately preserved parallel lamination, low-angle cross-lamination and wave ripple lamination, but in many cases this is at least partially destroyed by bioturbation which often becomes intense in the more argillaceous upper part of each sheet.

The lower part of the formation is well exposed at Cowbar Nab, to the west of the harbour, while the higher beds are more accessible to the east.

Staithes to Port Mulgrave

1A. Cowbar Nab. To visit this section, return to the main street and follow a footpath adjacent to the post office, cross Staithes Beck and turn right along the harbour wall. At the end of the wall the passage from the Redcar Mudstone Formation to the overlying Staithes Sandstone Formation is visible on the shore and adjacent cliff foot. In such a gradational sequence the placing of a boundary between the formations is rather arbitrary, but Howard (1985) has suggested it be drawn at the base of the 'Oyster Bed', which immediately underlies bed 1 of Howarth's (1955) section. Here the Oyster Bed is about 30 cm thick and very fossiliferous; bivalves dominate, including *Oxytoma inaequivalvis*, *Gryphaea depressa* and *Pseudopecten aequivalvis*. Above, bed 1 is a 1.4 m thick intensely bioturbated, argillaceous sandstone that lies at the foot of the cliff. The next few metres of siltstones and interbedded fine sandstones are accessible and include occasional *Oistoceras*, an ammonite characteristic of the upper part of the *davoei* Zone.

IB. Eastern side of Staithes Harbour. The higher part of the Staithes Formation forms the lower part of the cliff and adjacent scars. Higher in the cliff the individual ironstone bands of the Cleveland Formation stand out clearly. In the vertical faces at the cliff foot all the sedimentary features noted above can be seen. On adjacent scars ripple-marked surfaces are visible and sideritic concretions preserve large numbers of the bivalves *Protocardia truncatum*, *Oxytoma cygnipes* and *Gryphaea depressa*, and the scaphopod *Dentalium giganteum*.

Several minor faults occur here, especially in a small recess in the cliff known as Hartle Loop, about 150 m east of the harbour.

1C. Penny Nab. Eastwards towards Penny Nab the Staithes Formation becomes increasingly argillaceous upwards until it grades into the cyclic sediments of the overlying Cleveland Ironstone Formation. The base of the latter formation (and of the Penny Nab Member) is taken at the base of the first cycle (Howard, 1985), i.e. at the base of Howarth's (1955) bed 24. This is a row of scattered siderite mudstone nodules, sometimes packed with small ammonites (*Amaltheus stokesi*), occurring round the foot of Penny Nab at the base of a sloping ledge. A few paces to the northeast of this ledge a series of parallel grooves in the shale at regular 1.2 m (4 feet) intervals marks the line of an old tramway for transporting ironstone to a shallow dock northwest of the Nab (Owen, 1985, figure 2).

Locality 2. Jet Wyke to Brackenberry Wyke (Cleveland Ironstone Formation).

In the type area of the Cleveland Hills the Cleveland Formation contains thick ironstone seams which were formerly mined extensively. The ironstones thin and the intervening shales thicken towards the coast, where the formation is excellently exposed in Jet Wyke and round Old Nab into Brackenberry Wyke. Here, it consists of 25.3 m of shales and thin siltstones with sideritic and chamositic ironstone seams, some of which are oolitic in texture. Most seams cap coarsening-upwards cycles up to 7 m thick (Figures 7, 8), and individual cycles are laterally continuous over much of the basin (Rawson, Greensmith & Shalaby, 1982; Howard, 1985). The upper part of some cycles is striped with thin fining-upwards sheets, sometimes with basal gutter marks, probably deposited under storm conditions ('tempestites'). The formation is divided into the predominantly shaly Penny Nab Member (18 m) and the more ferruginous Kettleness Member (7.3 m) (Howard, 1985).

2A. Jet Wyke. The whole of the Cleveland Formation is accessible here, though the highest beds are better examined around Old Nab. The succession dips gently eastwards and several faults repeat parts of it, in one case bringing ironstone against ironstone in the middle of the Wyke to create a very extensive ironstone pavement on the shore. A detailed lithological sequence was given by Howarth (1955) and this has been combined with more recent sedimentological work to show the whole sequence as a log (Figure 7). The lowest ironstone, the Avicula Seam, forms a flat ledge starting about 150 m east of Penny Nab. Its upper surface shows many specimens of *Oxytoma* (formerly *Avicula*) *cygnipes*, while the base is conglomeratic.

Further east, the 'upper striped bed' of Greensmith, Rawson and Shalaby (1980) is often cleanly exposed at the cliff foot immediately beneath the thin (10 cm) Raisdale Seam ironstone. This bed (about 2 m thick and forming the upper part of bed 34) consists of a series of delicately preserved layers of pale coloured, laminated siltstone fining-up to darker mudrock (Figure 8). Each layer has an erosive base and gutters are developed at the base of some, cutting down into, and even undercutting, up to six underlying layers. The bed can be traced from the cliff foot onto the scars towards Old Nab, where the lighter, hard bases of the anastomosing gutters are seen in plan to be up to 0.5 m wide and 5 m long with an orientation almost due east-west. Similar gutters in the correlative bed at Hawsker (20 km to the southeast) are much less deep and have a finer-grained infill as if they are more distal from the shoreline, indicating currents from the west. The sequence at both localities suggests deposition under storm surge conditions.

Along the eastern side of the wyke the Pecten Seam is seen in vertical section to be represented by five thin layers of ironstone separated by thin shale partings. The base of the seam is taken as the base of the Kettleness Member. Above this level the former mining of the overlying Main Seam is evident higher in the cliffs, marked by a series of adits into which the overlying shales have collapsed.

2B. Old Nab. The regular blocks at the tip of this prominent headland are again the result of ironstone mining; pillars of Main Seam ironstone left as roof supports have since been unroofed by marine erosion. On the east side of the Nab shale backfill can be seen filling an adit running into the cliff. In the immediate vicinity of the Nab and into Brackenberry Wyke the Main Seam bedding surfaces show extensive networks of *Rhizocorallium* (crustacean) burrows, most of them showing scratch marks made by the crustaceans' claws.

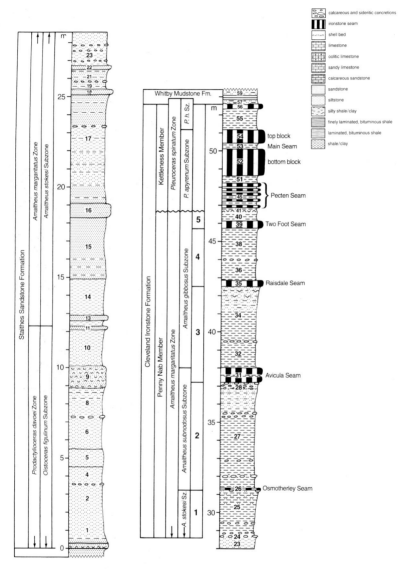

Figure 7. Lithic log of the Staithes Sandstone and Cleveland Ironstone Formations at Staithes. (From Rawson & Wright, 1996, fig. 22; based mainly on data in Howarth, 1955; Howard, 1985; Knox et al, 1991). The key is to Figures 7, 9, 18, 19, 21, 29 and 35. (Reproduced by permission of the Geological Society).

Figure 8. The Cleveland Ironstone Formation in Jet Wyke. (Upper) General view. The ironstone pavement in the foreground is the Avicula Seam. The shales above coarsen upward into a more silty sequence, the 'Upper Striped Bed', which is capped by the Raisdale Seam (R) across the middle of the photograph. The next hard band is the Two Foot Seam, followed by the five thin ironstone ribs forming the Pecten Seam (P), visible at the top of the photograph. (Lower) Close-up of the upper part of the 'Upper Striped Bed', showing fining-upward sheets with erosive bases. Well developed gutters are particularly prominent at the level indicated by the lens cap (3 cm diameter). The base of the overlying Raisdale Seam is conglomeratic.

2C. West side of Brackenberry Wyke. Here, the higher part of the Cleveland Formation is gently arched so that the lowest beds are seen about halfway along the cliff. Mine adits are again visible and ironstone was also quarried from the shore. There are good exposures of bedding surfaces of the Pecten and Main Seams, the former crowded with *Pseudopecten aequivalvis* and the latter riddled with *Rhizocorallium* burrows. Towards the head of the Wyke the ironstone nodules of bed 56 form the last ironstone platform. They contain body chambers of *Pleuroceras hawskerensis* plus numerous bivalves (*Pleuromya costata* and *Gresslya*) still preserved in burrowing position.

Locality 3. Brackenberry Wyke to Port Mulgrave (Whitby Mudstone Formation).

3A. Southwest side of Brackenberry Wyke. Just above bed 57 of the Cleveland Formation a sharp facies change marks the basal Toarcian transgression. The Grey Shale Member of the Whitby Mudstone Formation consists of grey micaceous mudstones with concretionary horizons. The lower part contains six bands of red-weathering sideritic concretions which cross the rocky platform at the south end of the Wyke. Here, the shingle on the shore above consists largely of nodules derived from various levels in the Whitby Mudstone Formation and is a good source of ammonites. It is better to collect here than to remove *in situ* specimens.

3B. The Sheep Stones. On the southern corner of Brackenberry Wyke the shore is strewn with well-weathered blocks of sandstone that have fallen from the Saltwick Formation at the top of the cliff. On walking round this area note that the more easterly blocks in particular are often firmly embedded on shale stacks up to half a metre high. These are the Sheep Stones, which have been interpreted to represent an ancient fall that took place when the rocky intertidal platform and mean sea-level were slightly higher, probably during the Ipswichian (= penultimate) interglacial period (Agar, 1960). Since the last (1992) edition of this guide part of this area has been covered by massive cliff-falls which extend round to the adjacent part of Thorndale Shaft. The initial fall was composed mainly of material from the Alum Shale Member of the Whitby Mudstone Formation and yielded abundant nodules with *Dactylioceras*, belemnites and even crustaceans. Nodules can still be found, but most of the rock has been either washed away or covered by a new fall composed of blocks of sandstone from the Saltwick Formation. This latest landslip has carried away part of the Cleveland Way at the top of the cliff, and is still moving.

3C. Thorndale Shaft. The shales on the shore to the southeast of the rock falls belong to the upper part of the Grey Shale Member. The characteristic ammonite *Dactylioceras tenuicostatum* occurs mainly in nodules which have been extensively collected, so that some of the principal nodule beds are represented by lines of hollows in the scars. The highest beds contain *D. semicelatum*, joined in the top 1.8 m by *Tiltoniceras antiquum* (see section in Howarth, 1973). Towards the cliff foot the Jet Rock, the lowest informal division of the Mulgrave Shale Member

Staithes to Port Mulgrave

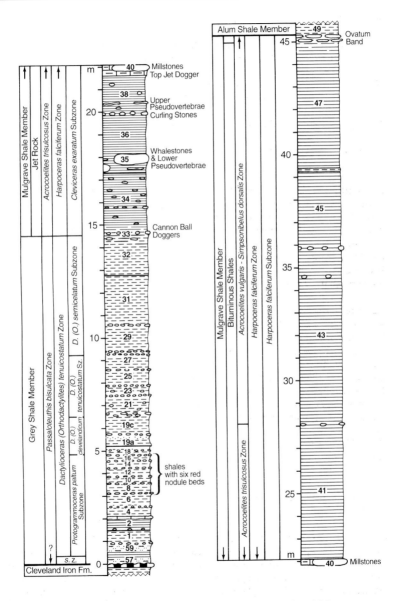

Figure 9. Lithic log of the Grey Shale and Mulgrave Shale Members: Port Mulgrave to Whitby. (From Rawson & Wright, 1996, fig. 23; based mainly on data in Howarth, 1962, 1992). (Reproduced by permission of the Geological Society).

(Figure 6), outcrops and forms the whole of the accessible lower part of the cliff between here and Port Mulgrave harbour. The Jet Rock is a finely-laminated, richly pyritic, dark-coloured, bituminous shale with numerous concretions either in beds or randomly scattered. These are usually pyrite-skinned, very hard and splintery and therefore very dangerous to hammer. There are four main marker beds here, the Cannon Ball Doggers (which form the base of the member), Whalestones, Curling Stones and Top Jet Dogger (Figure 9). A mine adit in the cliff face provides a good reference point; the thin (25 cm) stone band forming the roof of the adit is the Top Jet Dogger, which marks the top of the Jet Rock. Thus jet should be searched for in the lower part of the cliff. It occurs as long, compressed seams, lustrous black in cross-section, and is most easily found after winter storms when cliff falls have occurred. Later in the year the former position of seams is marked by small excavations in the cliff face! The specialised bivalve *Pseudomytiloides dubius* is common here, and flattened, pyritised ammonites are visible on the scars.

3D. Port Mulgrave. Port Mulgrave harbour was built in 1856-7 to ship ironstone worked from the shore and adjacent mines to the iron works of Tyneside. The bricked-up entrance to the main mine roadway (Seaton Drift) is visible in the cliff. Plans of the mining area and detailed information on the history of the mining are given by Owen (1985).

3E Rosedale Wyke. The Grey Shale and Mulgrave Shale Members form the rocky platform here (Figure 6), and show the same marker beds seen in the previous exposure. The Jet Rock was formerly quarried from the shore and the main marker beds are readily traced. Note in particular the Curling Stones, large rounded concretions that the jet miners left as stacks on the shore (Hemingway, in Hemingway *et al.*, 1968, p. 10). Above are the Millstones, lenticular doggers of limestone up to 3 m in diameter set in the upper surface of the Top Jet Dogger; these occur close to the cliff foot in the middle of the Wyke. Return from here to the adjacent harbour where a path up the cliff leads to a footpath (the Cleveland Way) back to Staithes. Alternatively take the narrow road (where there is parking for a car or minibus) leading to the main road (A174) at Hinderwell. This is the shorter route for a coach pick-up, as a coach can park just off the main road, near the church, at NZ 791171.

ITINERARY 2

Saltwick Bay to Whitby

P.F. Rawson and J.K. Wright
(incorporating material by the late J. E. Hemingway)

OS   1:25,000 Outdoor Leisure Map Sheet 27
            1:50,000 Landranger 94 Whitby
GS   1:50,000 Sheet 35/44 Whitby and Scalby

This short excursion examines the Whitby Mudstone Formation and part of the Ravenscar group. It follows the cliff-top path from Whitby Abbey to Saltwick Bay, descends to the shore at Saltwick and returns along the base of the cliffs to the east side of Whitby Harbour (Figure 10). The going is generally easy, though the shales can be very slippery. **This is strictly a low tide itinerary and it should not be started on a rising tide. Both Saltwick Nab and the headland immediately east of Whitby harbour can be rounded only within one to two hours either side of low tide.**

Parking is available in the Abbey car park or on the large harbour-side car park on the opposite (western) side of the harbour. From the Abbey car park follow the road eastward and then join a footpath in front of the adjacent farm, leading to the cliff-top path. Continue eastward, eventually passing by a caravan park to a footpath leading down to Saltwick Bay at NZ 915108. From the cliff-top note that in the upper part of the cliff the Saltwick Formation is exposed, and is here dominated by massive sandstones. From the same viewpoint one can contrast the form of Saltwick Nab with that of Black Nab. The former has been rapidly eroded since 1940, after a period of relative stability before the war, and will be reduced to a stack eventually. Black Nab is now only a stump of shale; the remaining pedestal of three stacks were eroded in the storm surge of January 1953.

Locality 1 Saltwick Bay (Mulgrave Shale Member).

Descend the cliff by the well-marked track. Near the beach, a pre-glacial channel with a near-vertical west bank and a gentler eastern slope is entirely filled with boulder clay. It persists seawards as a deep channel (Saltwick Hole) which is particularly noticeable at low tide. On the adjacent shore, many of the sandstone blocks represent the remains of a small quay, built to serve the adjacent alum quarries. There is a large overgrown quarry in Alum Shale on the cliff immediately south of Saltwick Nab, and a smaller one south of Black Nab. Heaps of red, burnt shale, overgrown soaking-pits and the ruins of the quay, as well as the size of the quarries here and elsewhere in this region, are an indication of the importance of the alum industry, which flourished during the sixteenth to nineteenth centuries. The history of the industry is described by Fox-Strangways (1892, pp 452-5).

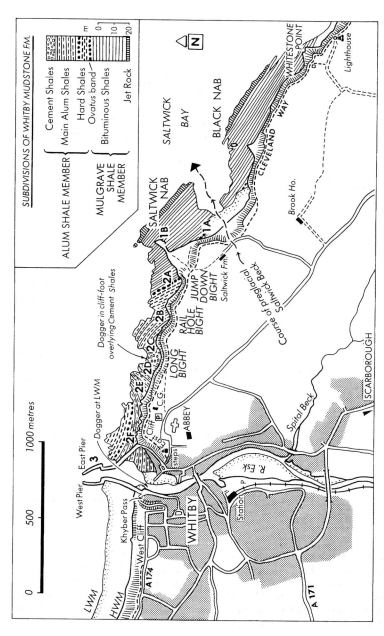

Figure 10. Map of Saltwick Bay to East Cliff, Whitby (Itinerary 2).

Saltwick Bay to Whitby

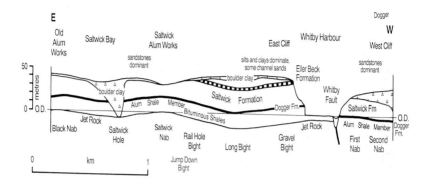

Figure 11. Cliff section at Whitby, as seen from the shore.

The shales that crop out so extensively in Saltwick Bay belong to the Mulgrave Shale Member, mainly to the Bituminous Shales (Figures 10, 11). Howarth (1962) has published a detailed bed-by-bed account of the sequence here, which is summarised in Figure 9.

1A. The highest of the three informal divisions of the Mulgrave Shale Member, the Ovatum Band, occurs near the foot of the cliff within the north end of Saltwick Bay, rising to the north-west towards Saltwick Nab. This is a distinctive 25 cm thick double band of pyrite-skinned, discoidal sideritic concretions that yield rare *Ovaticeras ovatum*.

IB. In a traverse of the rocky shore from the Ovatum Band towards low water mark to the east of Saltwick Nab, one crosses downward over the whole of the Bituminous Shales. There are only a few nodular horizons in these laminated beds, so the fossils are normally flattened - and often pyritised. Dactylioceratid and harpoceratid ammonites include the subzonal form *Harpoceras falcifer*. The bivalve *Pseudomytiloides dubius* is common, especially near the end of Saltwick Nab, where it also occurs uncrushed on the surface of concretions.

Near low water is a well-marked reef made of a tough, impure limestone (the Top Jet Dogger) that marks the top of the lowest division of the Mulgrave Shale Member, the Jet Rock. This limestone is characterised by large (up to 4.2 m in diameter) discoidal concretions, the Millstones, set in the top surface of the limestone. Note the very well marked jointing of this bed and the adjacent shales. Below it, the Jet Rock was formerly worked extensively for jet here, even though it is accessible only at low water spring tides.

Figure 12. ?Stegosaur *footprints at Locality 2C. Photograph kindly supplied by*
  Dr M. A. Whyte, University of Sheffield (from Whyte & Romano, 1993,
  fig. 4). The hammer is 35 cm long.

Locality 2. Saltwick Nab to Whitby Harbour (Whitby Mudstone, Dogger and
Saltwick Formations).

Walk round Saltwick Nab, or over the notch near its neck - but note that the shales
at the latter are steep and very slippery; the best footing is on some of the more
barnacle-covered shale 'steps'.

This excellent section is only a mile long, but great care must be taken in timing
the walk as one can only get round Saltwick Nab within 1 to 2 hours of low tide,
and it is easy to get cut off by the returning tide beneath the coastguard station at
East Cliff, close to Whitby Harbour wall (2E below). **There is no way up the cliff
between the two ends.**

Saltwick Bay to Whitby

The section provides an upward traverse through the Bituminous Shales and the Alum Shale Member of the Whitby Mudstone Formation. The overlying Dogger and Saltwick Formations are also accessible.

2A. Jump Down Bight. This is the first embayment west of Saltwick Nab. In the eastern part the Bituminous Shales are exposed again. Above them, in the southernmost corner of the bay, the Ovatum Band is visible in the base of the cliff, and from there it can be traced northwestward across the foreshore. Some of the discoidal concretions are set in larger sheets of reddish-weathering sideritic limestone, and occasional large masses of belemnite-limestone up to 7 cm thick also occur. The shales above belong to the Alum Shale Member, which again is informally divided into three units (Figure 10). The lowest, the Hard Shales, forms the foreshore in the western half of Jump Down Bight. These shales are not laminated like the underlying beds. This upward change in lithology reflects a return to better-oxygenated conditions on the sea floor. Mud-burrowing bivalves gradually return and become common higher in the sequence, in the Main Alum Shales. Two red-weathering, sideritic beds form useful markers here; a continuous 0.2 m thick bed (bed 50 of Howarth, 1962) crosses the shore obliquely about 40 m north-east of the small headland separating Jump Down Bight from Rail Hole Bight and marks the top of the Hard Shales, while about 5 m higher in the succession a 0.15 m thick bed of lenticular sideritic ironstone (bed 52) within the Alum Shale Member runs into the base of the cliff at the headland. Between the two bands *Dacryomya ovum* first becomes common, and belemnites are abundant and well-preserved here.

2B. Rail Hole Bight. The Main Alum Shales are well exposed on the shore, and are very fossiliferous. Belemnites are common and abundant specimens of the thick-shelled, shallow-burrowing *Dacryomya ovum* occur both crushed and uncrushed, occasionally in sufficient abundance to form thin limestones. Some *Dacryomya* are in life position, as also are *Pleuromya* sp. The ammonites *Dactylioceras* and *Hildoceras* are common, but usually with only the outer whorl (body chamber) well preserved, the inner whorls being crushed within a calcareous mudstone concretion. As the sequence is traced upwards, towards the cliffs, the last true *Dactylioceras* (*D. athleticum*) are abruptly replaced by *Peronoceras*, a dactylioceratid with spinose, fibulate ribs.

In the cliff face, the Dogger Formation climbs the cliff eastwards with a largely channel-free Saltwick Formation succession above it.

2C. Headland between Rail Hole Bight and Long Bight. On the headland, the cliff is free of debris down to high water mark, and a buttress of Dogger projects from the base of the cliff. Immediately below the Dogger, 10 m west of the northernmost tip of the headland, is the fallen block displaying the dinosaur footprints described and illustrated by White & Romano (1993). The prints were made in a red, iron-rich silt containing *Unio*, and were infilled with medium grained sand. A block of the resulting sandstone resting on sideritic siltstone rotated as it fell down the cliff, leaving the silt uppermost. As the silt weathers away it leaves the sandstone-filled prints in high relief (Figure 12). The footprint trail runs in a line heading straight for Whitby Pier. It consists of at least eight prints showing the broadly triangular, three-toed hind feet and the smaller, crescentic forefeet. Recent studies of the footprints suggest that they were made by a stegosaur (Whyte, personal communication, 1999). Take care not to damage this block; it is already suffering some sea erosion and growth of seaweed. Twenty metres east of the headland is a block with interesting three-toed bipedal dinosaur footprints, some showing a peculiar dragging of the foot. A large block with similar bipedal prints is in Whitby Museum. The cliff is rather unstable here, and further falls may well reveal further interesting footprint trails.

2D. Long Bight. Past a rock-fall opposite the wreck of a concrete ship on the shore, this next small embayment is occupied by a shallow syncline which has brought the upper part of the Alum Shale Member, known as the Cement Shales, down to shore level. These form the highest part of the Whitby Mudstone Formation here. The shales obtain their name from the abundant calcareous nodules at this level. They yield *Catacoeloceras* and, less commonly, *Hildoceras bifrons* and *H. hildense*. There are also abundant belemnites, mainly *Salpingoteuthis*.

The disconformably overlying Dogger Formation forms a shelf dipping gently west near the base of the cliff. Here the formation is a tough, very pebbly sideritic sandstone, 0.4 m thick. Abundant U-shaped tubes allied to *Arenicolites* or *Diplocraterion* descend from the base of the Dogger Formation into the Alum Shale Member. Four metres above the Dogger Formation, within the non-marine Saltwick Formation, a bed dominated by thick horizontal stems of carbonised wood has been worked for coal. Blocks of a fine-grained sandstone, fallen from a horizon 5.7 m above the Dogger Formation and containing paired valves of *Unio kendalli*, sometimes gaping, may equate with the freshwater shell-bed originally described at Saltwick (Jackson, 1911).

The western side of Long Bight is occupied by a large rock-fall consisting of blocks of pale grey, fine-grained sandstone with concretions of sideritic mudstone. These have fallen from just above the Dogger as it rises westwards in the cliff. They yield a flora including *Coniopteris*, *Williamsonia*, *Baiera* and *Czechanowskia*, and are known as the Whitby Plant Bed. The thickness is 3.5 m. The bed exhibits much contemporaneous microfaulting and is evidently an offbank deposit laid down under quiet conditions marginal to a channel which is seen further west.

2E. Cliffs below the Coastguard Station. As the plant bed is traced westwards, it passes into cross-bedded channel sandstone displaying easterly-dipping epsilon cross-bedding. Erosion at the base of this channel has thinned the Dogger Formation almost to nothing. Westwards, the cross-bedded channel sandstone passes rapidly into thin, level-bedded sandstone laid down marginal to the channel, which was migrating eastwards, the cross-sets being laid down as point bar deposits on the inside of a migrating meander. On the shore, the traverse from Long Bight to Whitby Harbour goes down the Alum Shale succession again.

2F. Coastguard Station to East Pier. The small headland beneath the coastguard station is the critical point for access back to Whitby. The sea is only free of the cliff here for about two hours either side of low water, and great care must be taken not to get cut off. Note the strongly developed north-south jointing, both vertical and inclined, which controls the cliff recession. All stages of cliff erosion from the widening of joints to the formation of vertically walled caves, capped by the Dogger Formation, may be seen.

On the main part of the shore here, the Hard Shales crop out (Figure 10). Above, the Main Alum Shales are exposed on the highest part of the shore and at the cliff foot, and contain scattered fragments of wood up to 2 m long. These are thickly coated with pyritic mudstone, the product of anaerobic decay, and may show either well-preserved cellular tissue infilled with calcite or barytes, or crushed and carbonised woody tissue preserved as poor grade jet. Again *Dacryomya ovum* is abundant. Higher still are the Cement Shales, overlain by the Dogger and Saltwick Formations.

From the western end of the section climb onto the concrete breakwater beneath the footbridge linking East Pier with the mainland, and descend the breakwater into Whitby Harbour. If the tide allows, turn right and proceed up the adjacent steps and a ramp onto Whitby East Pier. (Alternatively turn left inside the harbour, and walk along the sands to the steps leading into the adjacent old town).

Locality 3. Whitby East Pier (Alum Shale Member and Whitby Fault).

From the foot of the East Pier Lighthouse, contrast the succession of the East Cliff (52 m thick) with that of the West Cliff (23 m thick). To the east, the rock platform and lower cliff expose 12 m of Alum Shales. These are succeeded by a thin representative of the Dogger Formation (0.75 m) which is followed by the fine sandstones, siltstones and carbonaceous clays of the Saltwick Formation (31.4 m). There follows the marine Eller Beck Formation (*c.* 6 m), which is capped by glacial till or 'boulder clay' (Figure 10). The Alum Shale Member may be traced, at low tide, within the harbour at Collier Hope and also to the east of the West Pier.

By contrast, the West Cliff and Khyber Pass reveal a solely non-marine sequence of channel sandstones stacked one above the other. Because of this striking difference, a NNE-SSW fault with a westerly downthrow of 61 m was postulated along the deep channel of the harbour. The West Cliff succession was thus assigned to the Cloughton Formation in the middle of the Ravenscar Group (Fox-Strangways & Barrow, 1915). However, subsequent detailed mapping (Hemingway, 1953), particularly of the Dogger Formation, as well as borehole evidence within the harbour, shows that the fault (which is not exposed) downthrows no more than 12 m to the west. The West Cliff succession is thus a part of the Saltwick Formation, a conclusion which has been confirmed by spore analysis (Harris, 1953). Osborne (1998, pp. 266-286) gives a detailed account of the history of research into the Whitby Fault. Alexander (1986) has proposed that the fault was active in Mid Jurassic times, and that on the downthrow side to the west was a persistent, low-lying area repeatedly occupied by river channels. This would explain the succession of infilled channels visible to the west, whereas the Saltwick Formation to the east is largely level-bedded.

There is no public access to the bridge leading from the East Pier to the mainland. Return down the ramp and steps into Whitby Harbour. At the base of the cliffs are numerous fallen blocks of the Dogger Formation, which is 0.9 m thick here. Rotated blocks display excellently the basal conglomerate of pebbles derived by erosion of concretions in the underlying Whitby Mudstone Formation. Proceed over the sands to steps leading to Whitby Old Town, and thence to the 199 steps back to the Abbey and car park. It is well worth exploring the streets of the old town, where there are shops selling fossils and Victorian and modern jet jewellery, and a restored jet workshop.

Note: As an alternative to starting the itinerary in Saltwick Bay, especially when a neap tide allows very little time to get round Saltwick Nab, it is possible to park in Whitby, walk along the shore from East Pier to the West Side of Saltwick Nab as the tide falls, and then follow the whole of the succession back towards Whitby, through localities 2 and 3 only.

ITINERARY 3

Robin Hood's Bay

P.F. Rawson and J.K. Wright

OS   1:25,000 Outdoor Leisure Map Sheet 27
          1:50,000 Landranger 94 Whitby
GS   1:50,000 Sheet 35/44 Whitby and Scalby

Robin Hood's Bay provides excellent exposures of the Redcar Mudstone Formation and, in the central part of the bay, of Devensian (Pleistocene) tills. Although it is convenient to describe it as a single itinerary because of its geological unity, Robin Hood's Bay is large (6 km from North Cheek to Peak Steel) and individual beds may be traced for up to 2.5 km around it. Hence it is neither practical nor necessary to follow the sequence the whole way round the bay in one day. In fact to do so would risk the very real possibility of being cut of by an incoming tide, which eventually reaches the base of the cliff right around the bay. Therefore, any excursion in the bay should be commenced only on a falling tide.

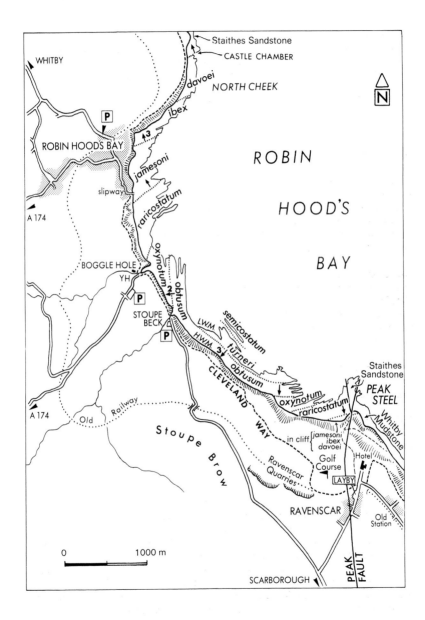

Figure 13. Map of Robin Hood's Bay and the Peak (Itinerary 3).

Robin Hood's Bay

The bay is accessible from four directions. Figure 13 indicates the roads and paths, together with car parks. From the south side, one can enter or leave by the route from Ravenscar to the beach described in Itinerary 4. There is a regular bus service from Scarborough to Ravenscar. Alternatively, one can drive over Stoupe Brow to Stoupe Beck, where a broad track leads to the beach. This road is narrow and the car park small, so that only cars or minibuses are suitable. The same is true for the larger car park at Boggle Hole, accessible from the Scarborough-Whitby road to the southwest. Robin Hood's Bay Town, with its car parks and shops, is accessible from the northwest. Buses from Scarborough and Whitby regularly visit the village.

Robin Hood's Bay is famed for its domed structure (Itinerary 4), the eastern and central part of the dome lying below sea-level. What remains has been carved by erosion into a huge half-amphitheatre, with the oldest beds cropping out at low water in the centre of the bay. Here they parallel the cliff face, so that the same few beds are exposed for a considerable distance. Hence the best way of examining the succession is to start somewhere in this area (approximately between Stoupe Beck and Miller's Nab) and work up the succession, to either the northwest or the southeast sides of the bay.

Both options have problems. Taking the northwestern route, one can follow the complete sequence past Bay Town round to North Cheek and Castle Chamber. However, having started at low tide in the centre of the bay, one has to be very careful of the rising tide, which rapidly returns to the cliff foot at Bay Town while the scars further towards Castle Chamber are still uncovered, thus cutting off the unwary. Therefore it may be necessary to follow the beds out of sequence. Senior (1994) has published a detailed itinerary for this part of the bay.

An alternative is to follow the southeastern sequence, either by driving to Stoupe Beck and working southeastwards towards the Peak, or by coming down the Peak and exploring the adjacent part of the bay back to the vicinity of Miller's Nab. The advantage of the last alternative is that one can combine this part of Itinerary 3 with a study of the Peak Fault and adjacent Whitby Mudstone Formation described in the first part of Itinerary 4, thus both entering and leaving the area at the Peak - though the return climb is a stiff one!

The sequence either side of the bay is essentially the same, except that on the northwest side of the bay the gradation from Redcar Mudstone Formation to the overlying Staithes Sandstone Formation can be seen at Castle Chamber, whereas on the southeastern side the highest part of the Redcar Mudstone Formation is faulted out at shore level by the Peak Fault.

Some 150 m of silty and shaly mudstones, siltstones and fine sandstones of Sinemurian and Pliensbachian age crop out in Robin Hood's Bay, representing the upper part of the Redcar Mudstone Formation. The lower part of the formation (Hettangian and basal Sinemurian) is not exposed, but some 90 m was encountered

Robin Hood's Bay

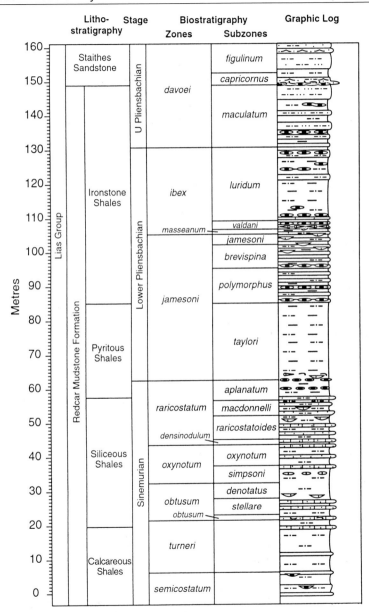

Figure 14. *Simplified lithic log of the Redcar Mudstone Formation, Robin Hood's Bay. Kindly provided by Dr S. Hesselbo (University of Oxford).*

in nearby boreholes. The exposed succession, and especially its sedimentology, have been the subject of considerable study in recent years (Van Buchem & McCave, 1989; Van Buchem, Melnyk & McCave, 1992; Van Buchem, McCave & Weedon, 1994; Hesselbo & Jenkyns, 1996). Fortunately, all these authors retain the informal subdivisions of Buckman (1915), who divided the Robin Hood's Bay succession into 4 units:

Ironstone Shales	64 m
Pyritous Shales	27 m
Siliceous Shales	38 m
Calcareous Shales	c. 20 m seen

Rather than document individual localities within the bay, we describe the successive units, highlighting the best areas to examine them. The locality map (Figure 13) shows the distribution of ammonite zones, as these provide a finer division than Buckman's lithological units; the correspondence between zones and lithology is shown in Figure 14. It is not feasible to reproduce the very detailed bed-by-bed logs published by Hesselbo and Jenkyns (1996), so the interested specialist should refer to that paper for further information. However, we are indebted to Dr S. Hesselbo for providing a simplified version (Figure 14) which gives a good impression of the whole sequence.

The Calcareous Shales are exposed in the low tide reefs in the centre of the bay, best seen on Flat Scars. They consist of silty mudstones with calcareous concretions and occasional thin but laterally quite extensive shell beds (mainly *Gryphaea*). The characteristic ammonites *Arnioceras* and *Caenisites*, with chambers filled with calcareous mudstone, can be found by careful search of the seaweed-covered reefs.

The Siliceous Shales swing round in a huge arc from Boggle Hole nearly to Peak Steel, forming the prominent reefs running out to sea just east of Bay Town. They get their name from the repeated occurrence of tough beds of calcareous siltstone and fine sandstone which form the more prominent, higher parts of individual scars. Hesselbo and Jenkyns (1996) place the base of the Siliceous Shales at the base of their bed 23, which is the first significant sandstone in the succession, forming a prominent ledge on the shore opposite Stoupe Beck. This lies a little below the top of the *turneri* Zone. The whole sequence was deposited on a shallow shelf, below fairweather wave base. The coarser-grained beds probably accumulated under storm conditions (see p.5), and are riddled with trace fossils such as *Rhizocorallium*, *Thalassinoides* and *Teichichnus*. Ammonites are quite common in the more argillaceous, quieter-water intervening beds, particularly the zonal form *Asteroceras obtusum*. Large body chambers of this species can be found weathering out of the shales in the rock platform (NZ 963032). *Gagaticeras*

Robin Hood's Bay

is a common indicator of the overlying *oxynotum* Zone; *Oxynoticeras* itself is rare in Yorkshire but occasional specimens can be found on the scars near Miller's Nab.

The last thin sandstone marks the top of the Siliceous Shales. The overlying Pyritous Shales mark a return to deeper water conditions. They yield frequent pyritic concretions, small pyritised ammonites, and thin-shelled bivalves which lived in dysaerobic (low oxygen) conditions. The best locality for fossils is the rock platform in the southeast corner of the bay (NZ 972025), where *Echioceras* (*raricostatum* Zone) is common. Opposite Robin Hood's Bay Town these beds, though present, are frequently covered with sand. In both areas the smoother topography of the intertidal platform contrasts with the 'scarp and dip' topography of the underlying beds.

The full succession of the Ironstone Shales can be examined only on the northwest side of the bay. Frequent bands of red-weathering sideritic nodules give the Ironstone Shales their name. Regular changes in climate controlled by Milankovitch cycles (cycles of variation in Earth's orbit) are thought to be responsible for the regular pale/dark banding in the lower part of the sequence, the so-called 'banded shales' (van Buchem *et al.* 1994). Seven Pliensbachian ammonite subzones are represented in these beds (Figure 14), but the ammonites are poorly preserved and sporadic. Among the genera represented are *Platypleuroceras, Tropidoceras, Acanthopleuroceras* and *Androgynoceras*. The large, semi-infaunal bivalve *Pinna* is common at some levels, usually flattened on the bedding planes, and current-swept belemnite accumulations occur. The Ironstone Shales become increasingly silty upwards, and grade almost imperceptibly into the silty sandstones of the Staithes Formation at Castle Chamber.

While much of the shoreline is rocky, the central stretch of the bay has some shingle and even sandy stretches too. Here the bulk of the cliff is formed of Devensian (last glaciation) tills. These are responsible for the huge variety of pebbles and boulders on the adjacent beaches, including blocks of Carboniferous limestones packed with corals, and 'indicator' erratics such as Shap Granite - brought here by ice from Shap Fell, in Cumbria.

A final word of caution. Robin Hood's Bay, though of great interest to the stratigrapher, sedimentologist or geomorphologist, can be disappointing to the fossil collector. Most of the beds were decalcified shortly after deposition, and most of the bivalves and ammonites are preserved only as mud-filled moulds. *Gryphaea* and *Pentacrinus* are the only fossils which regularly escaped decalcification. The exposures are picked over frequently by parties. Nevertheless, the keen geologist, braving the elements in winter, should be rewarded by interesting finds.

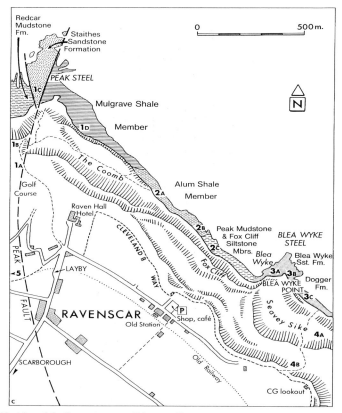

Figure 15. Map of the Ravenscar area (Itinerary 4).

ITINERARY 4

Blea Wyke Point and Ravenscar

J.K. Wright
with contributions by the late J.E. Hemingway

OS   1:25,000 Outdoor Leisure Map Sheet 27
          1:50,000 Landranger 94 Whitby
GS   1:50,000 Sheet 35/44 Whitby and Scalby

This is probably the most strenuous itinerary in the guide, especially as it
terminates with a 150 m (500 ft) climb back up the grassy cliffs. The route is along
the rock platform and over beach boulders for 2 km from Peak Steel to south of

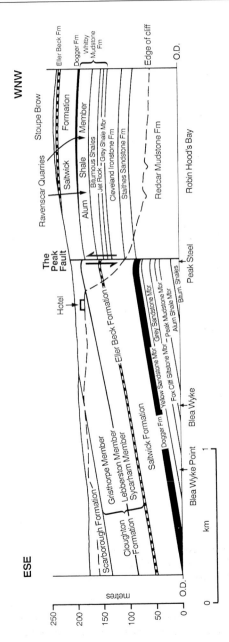

Figure 16. Diagrammatic section across the Peak Fault at Ravenscar, as seen from the shore.

Blea Wyke Point and Ravenscar

Blea Wyke Point (Figure 15). Several large rock falls and the boulder beach obscure some of the geology, and necessitate a little scrambling. The rock platform can be very slippery. Blocks of shale may fall unexpectedly, and hard hats should be worn. **Low tide is necessary to study much of the section.** High tide reaches the base of the cliff in several places, particularly at Blea Wyke Point, and care should be taken on a rising tide. Parking is available in the substantial layby at Ravenscar, overlooking Robin Hood's Bay, or alternatively southeastwards near the shop and cafe. There is a regular bus service to Ravenscar from Scarborough.

Locality 1. Ravenscar (the Peak Fault, Staithes and Whitby Mudstone Formations).

1A. Ravenscar Cliffs. From the entrance to the Raven Hall Hotel take the track to the left signposted to the shore. Cross the golf course and follow the signposted 'trail' into the cliff area. Just beyond the National Trust sign, the Staithes Sandstone Formation (Upper Pliensbachian) is seen on the left-hand side of the path. Micaceous sandstones, siltstones and a thin nodular ironstone are present and yield *margaritatus* Zone fossils. On the right-hand side of the path is a gully marking the line of the Peak Fault (Figure 16). On the eastern side of the fault there is a continuous sequence of strata beginning with an attenuated exposure of Yellow Sandstone (Upper Toarcian) succeeded by heavily jointed Dogger with pebble beds, then by massive sandstones, siltstones and a thin coal of the Saltwick Formation. Looking back at the Middle Jurassic beds from slightly lower down, note that although they are on the downthrow side, the Dogger being downthrown 90 m relative to its position on the west side of the fault, the beds dip down into the fault. This suggests that the fault-plane curves at depth (i.e. that it is listric). The alternative suggestion, that there has been a late compressive phase with reversal of movement on the fault, is not substantiated by examination of the joints close to the fault - movement on these was normal. The Peak Fault is now known to mark the western margin of the Peak Trough (p. 2). To the east, within the trough, a more complete Toarcian sequence is preserved than is visible anywhere else along the coast. Movement on the fault probably started during the Toarcian, and according to Alexander (1986), the fault was active, downthrowing to the southeast, during Mid Jurassic times, allowing a thick sequence of fluvial sands to accumulate in the subsiding area close to the fault. Further evidence of Mid Jurassic movement of this fault will be seen later.

1B. The view of Peak Steel and Robin Hood's Bay. Pause by the fence at the cliff-edge for the classic view of the Robin Hood's Bay Dome, with the reefs of Redcar Mudstone Formation swinging round through 180° (Figure 17 and Back Cover). The crest of the structural dome lies seaward of the coastline within the bay, but the truncated beds on its flanks form curving scars for a distance of five km to the northwest. Below, small faults branch out from the main Peak Fault, which splits into two smaller faults across the shore.

Figure 17. Robin Hood's Bay from the Peak. The curvature of the scars picks out the western flank of the Robin Hood's Bay Dome.

1C. Peak Steel. Follow the footpath down the fault gully to the shore arriving on the beach south of the Peak Fault, and proceed north to the fault, which is 25 m north of the ruins of the pumping station. A zone of crushed shale 10 to 20 cm wide in the base of the cliff marks the fault plane. Here, the Bituminous Shales (upper subdivision of the Mulgrave Shale Member) are faulted against Ironstone Shales of *jamesoni* Zone age containing bands of ironstone concretions. This indicates a throw of 153 m. The fact that the throw in the Liassic beds is 63 m greater than the throw of the Dogger at the top of the cliff is a clear indication of the amount of erosion which affected the western side of the fault prior to or contemporaneous with the deposition of the Dogger (Figure 16). Much of the Upper Toarcian sequence is absent west of the fault due to this erosion.

Where the Peak Fault bifurcates on the shore, the two branches bound a prominent triangular outcrop of Staithes Formation known as Peak Steel. The 'steel', which extends seawards for nearly 500 m at low water and is covered by high tide, is stepped between Redcar Mudstone Formation to the west and Whitby Mudstone Formation to the east. The reefs are mostly heavily covered with barnacles, and the sandstone is best examined nearest the cliff where this cover is minimal. Sideritic sandy limestone with profuse bivalves (*Protocardium truncatum*) alternates with fine-grained, ripple-drift laminated sandstone. To the east of the fault the Jet Rock (lower part of the Mulgrave Shale Member) is exposed among the boulders, the Top Jet Dogger being a calcareous mudstone very different from its development west of the fault. The Bituminous Shales are well exposed southeast of the fault (Figure 18).

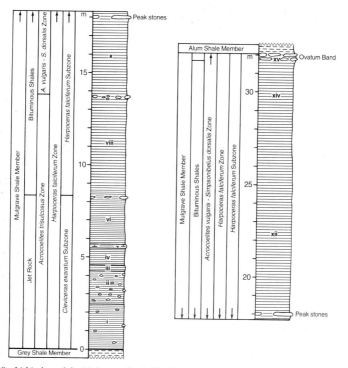

Figure 18. Lithic log of the Mulgrave Shale Member at Peak. (From Rawson & Wright, 1996, fig. 19; based mainly on data in Howarth, 1962). (Reproduced by permission of the Geological Society).

They are laminated and silty, and the ammonites (*Harpoceras falcifer*, *Dactylioceras* spp.) are completely flattened. Though scattered throughout, the bivalve *Pseudomytiloides dubius* is abundant in layers a few centimetres apart. The lack of infaunal bivalves and bioturbation, and the abundance of pyrite, indicates that the sea floor was generally anaerobic.

1D. The shore south of Peak Steel. Continue southwards for 250 m across the Bituminous Shales to reach a small bay where the Peak Stones (Figure 18) are well seen. These are low stacks, each capped by a discoidal concretion averaging 1.2 m in diameter and showing cone-in-cone structure, a post-depositional effect. Although these are similar to the concretions in the Top Jet Dogger to the west of the fault, they are here about 7.5m above the Top Jet Dogger level. The upward succession is almost continuously exposed for some distance in the cliff and in the mid-shore. Between 400 and 500 m south of the Peak Fault, the Ovatum Band (top of Mulgrave Shale Member), a double bed of pyrite-skinned concretions associated with calcareous lenses exhibiting cone-in-cone structure, is clearly visible in the cliff. It descends gently down to the base of the cliff 500 m south of

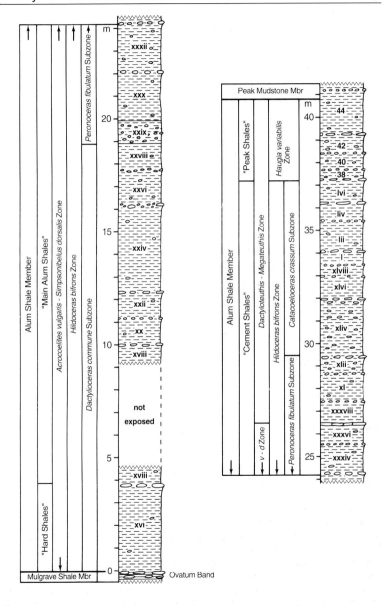

Figure 19. Lithic log of the Alum Shale Member at Peak. (From Rawson & Wright, 1996). (Reproduced by permission of the Geological Society).

the Peak Fault, and here it is well exposed in the rock platform. As well as occasional *Ovaticeras pseudovatum*, *Dactylioceras* spp. and *Phylloceras* sp. are also present in the concretions.

The succeeding Hard Shale unit of the Alum Shale Member is well exposed for a thickness of 4 m above the Ovatum Band. Like the Bituminous Shales, it contains flattened ammonites and *Pseudomytiloides dubius*, but it is not laminated. *Hildoceras bifrons* replaces the *Harpoceras falcifer* of the Bituminous Shales, and *Dactylioceras* spp. and belemnites are common. The next 7 m of shale is poorly exposed due to the large spread of boulders. These lie below a low, grassy undercliff which sometimes shows modern lacustrine sediments on its eroded edges. It is usually possible to walk along a path on the undercliff for about 250 m until shale is again visible on the shore at Locality 2. In summer, the vegetation may force one to keep to the shore.

Locality 2. The cliffs and shore east of the Raven Hall Hotel (Alum Shale, Peak Mudstone and Fox Cliff Siltstone Members).

2A. Northern shore exposures. The rock platform and cliff section for the next 150 m expose almost the whole 37 m thickness of the Alum Shale Member (Figure 19). The first 8.7 m belong to the *commune* Subzone. *Dactylioceras commune* is common, with *Dactylioceras* spp. and *Hildoceras sublevisoni*. The succeeding 5 m belong to the *fibulatum* Subzone. *Peronoceras fibulatum* and *Peronoceras* spp. are common, along with *Hildoceras bifrons*. The bivalve fauna has changed from that present at the last locality. Infaunal, bottom living forms such as *Dacryomya ovum* and *Gresslya donaciformis*, in life position, are commonly found. Bottom conditions during deposition of the Alum Shale clearly were not anoxic.

Further southwards, the lower Alum Shales, with their limited development of calcareous concretions, are succeeded by shales containing frequent bands of calcareous concretions. These are 12 m thick, forming the lower part of the cliff in the southern half of this exposure, and descending into the rock platform. This more calcareous facies of the Alum Shale Member is known informally as the Cement Shales. It belongs to the *crassum* Subzone, and *Catacoeloceras crassum* is abundant, along with *Hildoceras bifrons* and *Pseudolioceras lythense*. The sea floor was becoming more oxygenated with time, and *Gresslya donaciformis* and *Dacryomya ovum* are joined towards the top of the Cement Shales by small, well preserved *Trigonia literata*, again all in life position.

All these shore sections at Locality 2 vary in their accessibility, being sometimes covered with debris fallen from the cliff above. **The cliffs are in a very dangerous state at present and should be avoided.** On the rock platform, and in the beach gravel, there are numerous concretions enclosing ammonites. A more detailed description of the section is given by Howarth (1962). For those who do not wish to proceed further along this slippery, boulder-strewn shoreline, it is possible at this point to climb the low undercliff at NZ 985019 to pick up a path which winds its way up The Coomb to join the main path to Ravenscar.

2B. Southern shore exposures. After scrambling southwards over a large recent (1991) rockfall containing interesting blocks of Blea Wyke Formation sandstone and of Dogger, a further area of shale rock platform is reached. The lowest shale here was regarded as marking the base of the former 'Peak Shales' by Dean (1954). However, in a resurvey of these exposures (Knox, 1984), the lowest 6 m of shale at Locality 2B has been transferred into the Alum Shale Member as it is lithologically similar, containing almost no silt grains. The highest Alum Shale thus extends now into the *variabilis* Zone. Concretions are much less common, and ammonites are frequently preserved as mudstone-filled moulds. *Haugia* spp. are common, with rare *Catacoeloceras dumortieri*, *Lytoceras* sp., and *Denkmannia* sp. Numerous *Trigonia literata* are present, along with *Pleuromya* sp., *Gresslya donaciformis* and *Dacryomya ovum*, which dies out towards the top of the Alum Shale Member.

The Peak Mudstone Member (Knox, 1984) encompasses the succeeding 12.6 m of silty mudstone containing scattered fossiliferous concretions of siderite mudstone. Unfortunately, these very interesting beds are currently almost inaccessible due to erosion of the headland between localities 2B and 2C. It used to be possible to climb up this headland to collect fossils *in situ*. However, the characteristic concretions containing their profuse bivalve, ammonite and belemnite fauna can be found occasionally in the boulder-strewn beach. The subzonal ammonite *Grammoceras striatulum* (*thouarsense* Zone) is common, with a large variety of bivalves, including *Camptonectes* sp., *Ostrea* sp., *Pteria substriata*, *Protocardium* sp., *Pecten* sp. and *Inoceramus* sp.

The cliff here is known as Fox Cliff, and gives its name to the succeeding, highest member of the Whitby Mudstone Formation, the Fox Cliff Siltstone. At the southern end of the vertical cliff, more persistent siderite mudstone bands are visible between 9 m and 15 m up in the cliff. These bands mark the lower part of the Fox Cliff Siltstone, which is accessible at the next locality.

2C. Southern end of Fox Cliff. A section in the Fox Cliff Siltstone is easily accessibly 50 m south of locality 2B by traversing the beach boulders and climbing 10 m up the grassy base of the cliff. A 4 m section of silty shales with layers of siderite mudstone is visible. The typical ammonites *Pseudogrammoceras* and *Phlyseogrammoceras* of the *thouarsense* and *levesquei* Zones have been collected.

Proceed now over the poorly-exposed area of boulder-strewn beach into the centre of Blea Wyke (Norse: 'Vik' = narrow bay). There is a magnificent section of Ravenscar Group sediments in the cliff (the type-section). Excellent sedimentary structures may be found in fallen blocks. In particular, notice the blocks of a strikingly buff, fine grained sandstone showing slump structures, which have fallen from a horizon about 6 m below the base of the Scarborough Formation near the cliff top. Thin coals may readily be made out in the cliff.

Locality 3. Blea Wyke Point (Blea Wyke and Dogger Formations).

3A. The northern side of Blea Wyke Point. In the north face of the Point is the 9 m thick type-section of the Grey Sandstone Member of the Blea Wyke Formation. These high Toarcian sandstones and siltstones attain their maximum development here. The boundary between the Fox Cliff Siltstone and Grey Sandstone members is seen at the base of the cliff, almost in the wave cut platform, in the centre of Blea Wyke. There is a noticeable change from the darker siltstone to a paler, burrow-mottled sediment, with coarse silt and fine sand-filled burrows. The dense, smooth carbonate concretions of the Fox Cliff Siltstone are no longer present. The subzonal ammonite *Phlyseogrammoceras dispansum* (*levesquei* Zone) occurs in sandy concretions particularly in the lower beds within Blea Wyke. *Lingula beani* is present throughout and *Orbiculoidea reflexa*, *Dentalium elongatum* and *Homeorhynchia cynocephala* also occur. Belemnites are very common.

The two massive sandstones totalling 3.6 m in thickness, which cap the Grey Sandstone and form the wave-cut platform around the base of Blea Wyke Point, are known as the Serpula Beds (Rastall & Hemingway, 1940). They contain masses of the tubes of *Serpula deplexa* up to 30 cm across, which weather into burrs on the sandstone surface. The Serpula Beds are also characterised by an abundance of trace fossils which invest the rock almost completely. *Chondrites*, *Rhyzocorallium* and *Thalassinoides* are recognisable amongst the profusion of different types. Body fossils are most common in the topmost few centimetres, with *Phlyseogrammoceras* sp., *Homeorhynchia cynocephala*, *Pteria* sp., *Oxytoma* sp., and *Orbiculoidea reflexa* (Dean, 1954). **Note that the tide reaches the base of the cliff at Blea Wyke Point within 2 hours either side of high tide.**

3B. The southern side of Blea Wyke Point. The upper Yellow Sandstone Member of the Blea Wyke Formation is exposed in the cliffs just south of Blea Wyke Point. The facies of the Yellow Sandstone is very similar to that of the top two beds of the Grey Sandstone. The trace fossil assemblage is just as varied, but the beds have been more subject to subaerial weathering. They still reveal their original grey colour in the centre of blocks. These beds yield only a poorly preserved assemblage of body fossils, including *Dumortiera* spp., *Homeorhynchia cynocephala*, '*Terebratula*' aff. *trilineata*, *Gresslya* sp., *Modiolus* sp., *Pteria* sp., *Pinna cuneata* and *Trigonia* sp. (Dean, 1954).

3C. South of Blea Wyke Point. Continue southeast up the succession until the base of the Dogger is accessible in the low cliff. The junction of Dogger on Yellow Sandstone is marked by a sudden change to greenish-grey, shelly, sideritic chamosite oolite sandstone. This 40-45 cm thick basal bed of the Dogger is rich in '*Terebratula*' *trilineata*, with less common *Gresslya donaciformis*, *Trigonia ramsayi*, *Pentacrinus* sp. and fossil wood. There are also many derived Whitby Mudstone pebbles, some containing recognisable *Dactylioceras* and *Hildoceras*, and many Liassic belemnites. The bed is usually firmly cemented to the delicately bored surface of the Yellow Sandstone. The time gap in between is considered to be small, of the order of one subzone (Parsons, 1980).

This basal bed is succeeded by an extremely iron-rich bed which weathers back. Two further pebble beds are met with as one proceeds up the Dogger succession. A hundred metres southwards and round a small point the top of the Dogger is accessible. Three metres below the top is the Nerinea Bed, a lenticular shell-bed up to 30 cm thick rich in *Nerinea cingenda, Cerithium* sp., *Astarte* sp., *Trigonia* sp., *Gervillella* sp., etc. The original calcareous shells are replaced by siderite and weather into sharp relief from a matrix of sandy chamosite oolite. **This unique exposure, because of its excellence, should not be hammered.** Fossils can be collected readily from fallen blocks. Southwards, the surface of the Dogger Formation, here a sphaerosiderite passing down into a sandy, sideritic chamosite oolite, is deeply weathered, with prominent ribs marking the joints.

Locality 4. The Cliffs south of Blea Wyke (Ravenscar Group).

Three hundred and fifty metres south of Blea Wyke Point the low cliff ends, and it is possible to ascend via a narrow path leading across the undercliff. The way up begins at the point where the Dogger Formation disappears below sea-level at high tide. There is no 'made up' path here, but simply a route tramped down by fishermen and geologists over the years. In late summer the path is rather obscured by bracken, and care must be taken to avoid falling over loose boulders. The Eller Beck Formation makes a well marked feature 50 m above the Dogger Formation. A rope has been installed here to aid the ascent/descent, though this is not strictly necessary.

4A. Cliffs 600 m south of the path. The attenuated Lebberston Member is not exposed near the path but may be seen 600 m to the south about 27 m below the Scarborough Formation. The Lebberston Member here is essentially a ferruginous marine sandstone 3 m thick with siderite mudstones containing *Trigonia* sp., *Ostrea* sp. and *Haploecia straminae*.

4B. The upper cliff. After a second steep ascent, the path levels out, and swings sharply right below crags of sandstone and limestone (Gristhorpe and Scarborough Formations). A thin coal with seat-earth may be examined about 3 m below the base of the Scarborough Formation. Such coals, dominated by *Equisetum*, are frequently found at this level, but rarely exceed 0.5 m in thickness. The Scarborough Formation attains its maximum thickness of 35 m at Ravenscar, and is divisible into five main units as follows (after Parsons, 1977; Gowland & Riding, 1991):-

5. **Bogmire Gill Member**   m
    fine grained, flaggy sandstone with abundant
    moulds of *Pleuromya* sp.   4.5

4. **Ravenscar Shale Member**
    sandy shales with concretions rich in *Pseudomonotis*
    lycetti, *Perna sp.*, *Ostrea* sp. and belemnites.   17.0

3. **Spindle Thorne Limestone/Hundale Sandstone members**
    (*undifferentiated*)
    calcareous sandstones and impure limestones with *P. lycetti* and
    Gervillia scarburgensis.   5.5

2. **Hundale Shale Member**
    fine grained, flaggy sandstone with *Pleuromya* sp.   4.5

1. **Helwath Beck Member**
    thick, laminated sandstone showing cut-and-fill
    structures with frequent marine trace fossils including
    Diplocraterion   seen to 3.0

Unit 1 is now included in the Scarborough Formation (Gowland & Riding, 1991). Previously, it had been considered to be the highest unit of the Gristhorpe Formation (Parsons, 1977). Two massive beds of limestone from unit 3 stand out. Most of the fossils, which include *Lopha*, *Astarte*, *Pecten*, *Modiolus*, *Teloceras*, *Pentacrinus* and belemnites, are weathered and very fragile. The Ravenscar Shales and Bogmire Gill Member are now largely grass covered and cannot be examined without an excavation. Continue to the cliff-top and return to Ravenscar.

Locality 5. Ravenscar Brickworks (Fault-attenuated Whitby Mudstone Formation and Ravenscar Group successions).

The succession between Peak Steel and Blea Wyke Point, on the east side of the Peak Fault, should be contrasted with that in Ravenscar Brickpit 450 m west of the fault (NZ 973015). From the entrance to the Raven Hall Hotel proceed down the track heading southwestwards (Cleveland Way). Carry on down the main track, and fork left at the Nature Trail signpost 4, and proceed left under the archway under the abandoned railway. The area around the kilns has been fenced off as they have become dangerous. Proceed right around the kilns and into the brickpit. The high, inaccessible face shows a thin (1 m maximum) development of the Dogger Formation resting on Alum Shales. The Dogger is then overlain by level-bedded alternations of shale and sandstone of the Saltwick Formation. Many blocks of the Dogger have fallen to the quarry floor. Some contain bored pebbles of derived Liassic nodules. 'U' shaped *Diplocraterion* burrows, some superbly developed, penetrate the full thickness of the Dogger Formation from its top surface, being filled with coarse quartz sandstone. Many blocks of plant-rootlet sandstone have fallen from the Saltwick Formation, and from here Sargeant (1970, plate 21) figured a dinosaur footprint, referred to *Satapliosaurus*. Southeast of the quarry, close to the Peak Fault, the Dogger Formation thins out entirely. Some 57 to 58 m of beds, including also the Cement Shales, Peak Mudstone, Fox Cliff Siltstone and the Blea Wyke Formation, are absent on the western, upthrown side of the fault. The younger beds also show a marked reduction in thickness from east to west across the fault, the Saltwick Formation being reduced from at least 57 m to only 30 m and the Cloughton Formation from 77 m to about 55 m. The differences in the successions on the two sides of the Peak Fault are shown in the cross-section (Figure 16).

The omission of nearly 50 m of Liassic beds, and the attenuation of the Ravenscar Group by some 60 m, have been explained in two ways. Fox-Strangways and Barrow (1915) suggested that contemporary Jurassic movement on the Peak Fault allowed Upper Toarcian beds to be preserved on the downthrown side, while on the shallow upthrown side they were either scoured off or not deposited. Additional Mid Jurassic movement is necessary to account for the difference in thickness of the Middle Jurassic beds. In contrast, Hemingway (1974) and Hemingway and Ridler (1982) suggested that the successions had been laid down in areas which were initially some distance apart, and which had been brought together by transcurrent (lateral) movement along the Peak Fault, probably during the Tertiary. Sinistral movement would be necessary to account for the distribution of the beds.

A structural analysis of the Peak Fault Zone as it extends south to Cayton Bay shows that it can be interpreted as a transcurrent fault system, but one of dextral movement, not sinistral. The main northwesterly trending faults and the subsidiary NNE/SSW trending branch faults fit naturally a near north-south primary stress pattern. ESE/WNW trending secondary drag folds fitting this stress pattern can be recognised at Osgodby Nab (Wright, 1968, fig. 9) and at Hayburn Wyke. Limited dextral movement of the Peak Fault Zone is very likely but the major sinistral movement required by Hemingway's hypothesis is now considered unlikely.

Milsom and Rawson (1989) have traced the Peak Fault Zone into the offshore area, and define a Peak Trough, a zone of trough-faulting 5 km wide bounded to the west by the Peak Fault, and to the east by a series of faults running from Scarborough to Red Cliff. Normal faulting took place in the trough in Triassic, Mid Jurassic, probably Late Jurassic/Cretaceous and Tertiary times. Movement was by gentle creep rather than by sudden displacement, with attendant earthquake shocks, for much of the time. The surface expression of the trough may have been only a metre or two (Alexander, 1986) and as such the trough operated at Ravenscar for much of the Aalenian and Bajocian, allowing a succession to accumulate within the trough 60 m thicker than that on the western flank. The Peak Fault Zone now takes its place amongst the many other Mesozoic synsedimentary fault systems which have been discovered recently in the North Sea and in southern England.

Cloughton Wyke to Scalby Ness

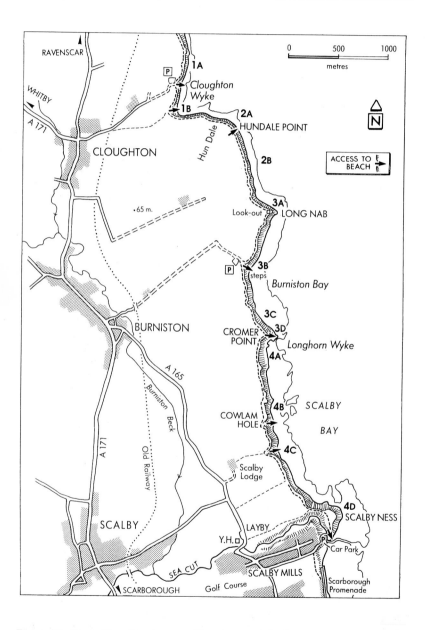

Figure 20. Map of localities between Cloughton and Scalby (Itinerary 5).

ITINERARY 5

Cloughton Wyke to Scalby Ness

J.K. Wright

OS   1:25,000 Outdoor Leisure Map Sheet 27
          1:50,000 Landranger 101 Scarborough
GS   1:50,000 Sheet 35/44 Whitby and Scalby

This itinerary provides a traverse through part of the Ravenscar Group, from the Lebberston Member (Millepore bed) to the Scalby Formation (Figures 20, 21). The full excursion involves a 5 km walk along the rock platform at the base of the cliffs and over stretches of beach boulders. The going can be quite strenuous. However,

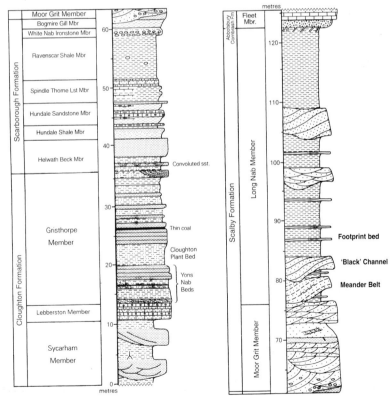

Figure 21. Lithic log of the Ravenscar Group between Cloughton Wyke and Scalby Ness. (Modified from Rawson & Wright, 1996, fig. 9). (Reproduced by permission of the Geological Society).

it is possible to avoid much of the more strenuous walking by ascending the cliff at convenient points and proceeding via the cliff top path. **A falling tide is necessary** to see the geology to its best advantage, particularly as the full sweep of the meander belt sandstone in Scalby Bay (Locality 4C) can only be seen within two hours of low tide. Other parts of the section are not accessible above mid-tide. It is possible to drive cars or minibuses down to the cliff top from both Cloughton and Burniston (Figure 20), though the car parks are small (half a dozen vehicles) and the roads narrow. At the start of the itinerary large parties will have to be dropped off in Cloughton. There is a regular bus service from Scarborough to Cloughton.

Locality 1. Cloughton Wyke (Lebberston Member to basal Scarborough Formation).

1A. The north side of Cloughton Wyke. Descend to the shore from the car park (which is 500 m north of the centre of Cloughton Wyke) and walk northwards over large fallen sandstone blocks (some of which show excellent sedimentary structures) for 250 m. Here the Lebberston Member, represented by the 3 m thick Millepore bed, forms a series of reefs running southeastwards out to sea. The bed consists of three tiers of shelly, calcareous sandstone and sandy limestone each forming a coarsening-upwards cycle. The middle tier is the most fossiliferous and the upper part is extremely hard where it is cemented by siderite. The fauna includes *Arcomya elongata, Lima duplicata, Entolium demissum, Pleuromya beani, Trigonia* sp., *Pholadomya saemanni* and *Modiolus imbricatus*. The branching bryozoan *Haploecia [Millepora] straminea*, which originally gave its name to this unit, is less common than at Osgodby Nab (Itinerary 7). Many of the shells are preserved in the white-weathering clay mineral dickite. Excellent cross-bedding makes the upper tier very distinctive. Compared with the sections south of Scarborough (Itinerary 7), the Millepore bed here shows a marked decrease in the content of ooliths and shell debris and an increase in calcareous sandstone and particularly iron carbonate, indicating that it accumulated nearer the shoreline (Bate, 1959).

Following a suggestion by Knox (personal communication), the succeeding Yons Nab beds are regarded here as the basal, quasi-marine part of the Gristhorpe Member. The Yons Nab beds are exposed in the low cliff on the way back towards Cloughton Wyke. Here quasi-marine beds interdigitate with fully non-marine beds. Resting on the Millepore bed is 0.6 m of ripple-drift cross-laminated sandstone, succeeded by 1.6 m of flaser-bedded, intertidal, shaly sandstone with numerous bivalves including *Trigonia, Pecten* and *Ostrea*. A variably bioturbated, ripple-drift cross-laminated sandstone (0.6 m) seems to complete the Yons Nab beds sequence. It is succeeded by 1 m of shale with coaly, carbonaceous layers, which weathers back readily.

However, traversing southwards across a large rock-fall, a low cliff is reached exposing, above the carbonaceous shale, a further 2.6 m of quasi-marine beds, an almost identical situation to that seen at Yons Nab (Itinerary 7). These consist of

Figure 22. The Scarborough and Scalby Formations, Cloughton. (Upper) The Scarborough Formation in the cliffs east of Cloughton Wyke. The sandstones and shales of the Helwath Beck Member form the lowest third of the cliffs. They are overlain by the thin bedded alternations of impure limestone and shale of the Hundale Shale, Hundale Sandstone and Spindle Thorne Limestone members. These are capped here by grass-covered glacial drift. (Lower) The Scalby Formation, looking NW from Long Nab into The Hundales. Fallen blocks of cross-bedded channel sandstone from the Long Nab Member occupy the foreground. In the cliffs behind, sandstones of the Moor Grit Member are succeeded by the shales and thin sandstones of the Long Nab Member.

Figure 23. An Equisetites *rootlet bed in the Gristhorpe Member, Cloughton Wyke.*

flaggy and well bedded sandstones containing occasional *Diplocraterion* burrows, and strongly bioturbated towards the base. These beds were first included within the Yons Nab sequence by Livera and Leeder (1981). The top of this unit forms a slippery ledge facing southwards and above it occurs a fully non-marine succession of 4.5 m of shales with thin coals and a rootlet bed, overlain by thick sandstone.

1B. Cloughton Wyke. The non-marine sandstones and shales of the upper part of the Gristhorpe Member are exposed in the cliffs and rock platform for the 0.5 km from the car park area southwards to the centre of Cloughton Wyke. The lower beds, occurring just above the sequence described at Locality 1A, are exposed in the cliffs on either side of the boulder-strewn beach below the car park. They consist of thick, planar-bedded sandstones, a facies unusual in the non-marine beds, and which is almost certainly the result of sheet flooding. This can be demonstrated by a close examination of these beds in the cliff between the car park and Cloughton Wyke. **The cliff is, however, unstable with considerable overhangs** (Figure 22), **and great care should be taken along this section.**

The planar-bedded sandstones generally occur in four half-metre tiers. Below the lowest tier there is a gradual shallowing-upwards sequence extending over a thickness of 1.5 m from shale with siderite nodule bands (the Cloughton Wyke Plant Bed) through silty shale into a thin-bedded, ripple marked sandstone.

Cloughton Wyke to Scalby Ness

The basal tier of massive sandstone infills grooves and flutes carved into the thin-bedded sandstone. The bottom structures indicate a current flow from NNE to SSW. The thick beds of sandstone thus appear to be associated with a large distributary channel to the northeast, which was subject to repeated breaches such that extensive sheet sands (crevasse-splays) spread southwestwards into the Cloughton Wyke area. Within each tier, though the bedding is frequently planar reflecting the strong current flow, ripples and cut-and-fill structures are also seen. Excellent sedimentary structures are to be found in the fallen blocks beneath the cliffs. After each episode of crevasse-splaying, the low lying area around Cloughton Wyke was then colonised by marsh plants. Well-preserved rootlets are visible in tiers 2 and 4 (Figure 23), and the highest tier is overlain by a thin coal.

The coal forms an excellent marker horizon, and can be followed, dipping gently southwards, into the base of the cliff in the centre of Cloughton Wyke. Here the top of the underlying fourth tier, heavily rooted, forms the upper rock platform. Above the coal comes 6 m of alternations of sandstone and shale. The sandstone resting on the coal is cross-bedded, though laterally persistent, and it is heavily load casted or even convoluted into the underlying coal and carbonaceous shale. Numerous 2 cm diameter sand-filled tubes extend down into the coal. These presumably are root structures.

There follows 2 m of alternations of shale and sandstone, often heavily rooted and convoluted. Above is a 3.5 m thick pale grey alluvial clay which immediately passes laterally into a channel sandstone, deposited rapidly and convoluted at its base. The top of the clay is rooted, and overlying it is a dark, laminated, shaly siltstone. The boundary between the two beds is clearly erosive on a small scale, and infilled burrows carry dark silt several centimetres down into the underlying grey clays. Gowland and Riding (1991) took this surface to mark the base of the Helwath Beck Member of the Scarborough Formation, and it thus marks the beginning of a marine transgression.

The shaly siltstones at the base of the Helwath Beck Member pass up into massive, convoluted sandstone; the combined thickness is about 2 m. The convolutions are thought to have been caused by an earthquake shock due to movement on the Peak Fault, here running 1.6 km to the west. The bed is remarkably persistent, and can be traced all the way to Ravenscar. The upper part of the member, comprising 4 m of extremely massive sandstone containing excellent marine trace fossils, forms the top part of the cliff in the centre of the wyke (Figure 22).

Amid the boulders on the shore, the medium-grey, micaceous, silty clays of the Cloughton Wyke Plant Bed can be traced from the base of the cliffs south of the car park to the centre of Cloughton Wyke, where they go below sea level. The plant bed is seen at its best in the middle of the rock platform half way between these localities. The flora is rich, usually carbonised, but occasionally preserved in a flexible, chitinous form. Individual species have a remarkably local distribution. They include *Ptylophyllum pecten*, *Cladophebis* sp., *Czechanowskia* sp., *Nilssoniopteris* sp. and *Otozamites* sp.

Cloughton Wyke to Scalby Ness

Locality 2. Hundale Point (Scarborough and Scalby Formations).

The walk over the boulder-strewn rock platform from Cloughton Wyke to Hundale Point is a little strenuous and should only be attempted at mid to low tide. An easier alternative is to ascend via steps and a step-ladder in the centre of Cloughton Wyke and walk along the cliff-top path to the easy descent at Hundale Point. **Do not attempt to descend to the beach at Hundale as there is a sheer drop.**

2A. North side of Hundale Point. About 70 m along towards Hundale Point, the junction of the Helwath Beck Member and the Gristhorpe Member is seen in the base of the cliff. The undulating, erosive contact of dark, silty shale on grey clay is well seen, dark, silt-filled burrows extending down into the Gristhorpe Member. In the flaser laminated, silty sands 0.5 to 1 m above the contact 'U' shaped *Diplocraterion* burrows occur. Just beneath the convoluted bed, hummocky cross bedding and climbing ripples in laminated sandstone indicate tidal scour in intertidal conditions.

After a further 30 m of scrambling over beach boulders, a wave cut platform in the channel sandstone referred to in Locality 1B is reached. The going is easier now. The massive upper sandstone of the Helwath Beck Member forms the lower middle of the cliff, and huge blocks of this sandstone litter the foreshore (Figure 22). The beautiful, laminated, scour-and fill cross-bedding is well seen in weathered blocks, with numerous *Diplocraterion* 'U' burrows, especially in the top 0.3 m.
Yet more scrambling over beach boulders is necessary to reach the top of the Helwath Beck Member, which reaches the rock platform just east of Hundale, and strikes out to sea, forming a small reef. Standing on the top of the Helwath Beck Member, with its profusion of 'U' burrows, one can see the stratigraphy of the remainder of the Scarborough Formation displayed in the rock platform and cliff.

The Hundale Shale Member (2.6 m) crops out between the boulders up to the base of the cliff. Its name is something of a misnomer, as it comprises intensely bioturbated silty sandstone in the lower part, passing up into argillaceous sandy limestone with *Gervillella*. The top is marked by a thin, distinctive, red-weathering, iron-rich bed.

The Hundale Sandstone Member (4.0 m), seen in the lower cliff, consists of two contrasting tiers of sandstone. The lower one is thin bedded, flaggy and argillaceous, intensely bioturbated, with *Rhizocorallium* and *Diplocraterion*. It is overlain by a more massive tier of sandstone which is less argillaceous. A thin bed of pink-weathering, sideritic limestone resting on shale separates the tiers. The top surface of the Hundale Sandstone is very shelly, with *Lopha* and '*Pentacrinus*' (compare with the Crinoid Grit, the lateral equivalent of these beds in the west of the Cleveland Basin).

The Spindle Thorne Limestone Member (3.7 m) consists of regular alternations of superbly bioturbated sandy shale with bioclastic, argillaceous limestone containing large bivalves. It descends gently to form the base of the cliff for several tens of metres round to Hundale Point.

The Ravenscar Shale Member (8.2 m) consists of a thick sequence of dark grey shales with small, fossiliferous concretions.

The White Nab Ironstone Member (1.3 m) is thinly developed here. It consists of sulphurous, grey, sandy shales with three layers of iron-rich concretions.

The Bogmire Gill Member (approx. 2.5 m) is much more marginally marine, consisting of siltstone passing up into fine grained sandstone. It is abruptly overlain by the cross-bedded sandstones of the Moor Grit.

The upper three members of the Scarborough Formation can be examined near the base of the cliff at Locality 2B.

2B. The cliffs south of Hundale Point. Immediately south of the path which leads from Hundale Point up to the cliff-top path, the Ravenscar Shale Member forms the base of the cliff for several tens of metres. The small, fossiliferous concretions in the grey shales yield frequent ammonites, including *Teloceras* sp. and *Dorsetensia* sp. The White Nab Ironstone Member can be a little difficult of access, tending to be hidden by scree. The inter-tidal, flaser bedded silts and fine grained sandstone of the Bogmire Gill Member can be reached by climbing the grassy slopes beneath the cliffs of Moor Grit. At the time of writing, the Bogmire Gill Member was also visible at the base of the cliff, in part of a huge, tilted, slipped block. The undulating, erosive base of the Moor Grit Member contains much charcoal and fossil wood.

The Scarborough Formation passes rapidly beneath beach level southwards, and the rock platform and cliffs all the way to Scarborough are composed of Scalby Formation sandstones and shales, overlain by glacial till. The 10 m thick sandstone unit comprising the Moor Grit Member forms the cliff along much of this bay south of Hundale Point, named The Hundales on recent OS maps (Figure 22). The Moor Grit Member shows spectacular 6 m high cross-bedded units indicating an E to NE current flow. A drawing of this cliff section appears in Nami and Leeder (1978). The coarse, mature sandstones are rich in coalified plant remains with subordinate charcoal fragments. The massive channel sands alternate with and pass laterally into off-bank laminated siltstones and crevasse-splay sheet sands which alternate with shale. The impression is of a rapidly accumulating series of beds, with little re-working or lateral migration of channels.

Locality 3. Burniston Bay (Scalby Formation).

3A. Long Nab. Proceed round the bay to Long Nab, the type-section of the upper member of the Scalby Formation. The Nab is protected from erosion by several huge blocks of cross-bedded sandstone up to 4 m thick derived from a channel in the lower part of the Long Nab Member (Figure 22). The cliff section on the south

Cloughton Wyke to Scalby Ness

*Figure 24. The Scalby Formation, Long Nab and Burniston Bay. (Upper) Saurian footprint
in a fallen block from the Burniston Footprint Bed, Long Nab. (Lower) Point-bar
sands infilling a channel in the meander belt in Scalby Bay. Stream direction
from left to right.*

Cloughton Wyke to Scalby Ness

side of Long Nab in Burniston Bay displays well the main features of the higher part of the member. There are alternations of fine clays and siltstones with occasional sand-filled channels. A small channel is seen in section at eye-level, cutting down half a metre into the underlying shale. The sandstones above are more persistent and even-bedded. At a height of 4 m above the rock platform occurs the well-known Burniston Footprint Bed. The dinosaur prints were made in soft, silty clay subsequently infilled by a gentle incursion of silt and sand, preserving the prints as casts. As blocks of this silty sandstone fall to the beach they frequently come to rest upside down at the foot of the cliffs, displaying the footprints very well (Figure 24). Two types were figured by Black *et. al* (1934). A comprehensive list and descriptions of footprint finds in the Scalby Formation was given by Ivens and Watson (1994).

The rock platform throughout the bay reveals a complex series of intersecting channel sandstones of the meander belt unit (Nami, 1976). Cross-bedding dips of 20° or 25° are common. The sands accumulated as point bar deposits on the inside bends of migrating channels. Thus the strike of the (epsilon) cross-bedding indicates the orientation of the channel, with the dip of the cross-bedding pointing down into the channel. Most of the cross-bedded units are curved in plan, showing the meandering nature of the stream complex, with later channels cutting down into and intersecting the bedding of earlier channels.

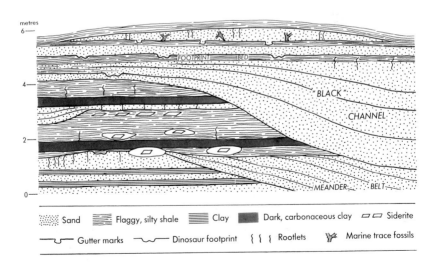

Figure 25. Diagrammatic section of the lower Long Nab Member, Burniston and Scalby Bays.

Cloughton Wyke to Scalby Ness

3B. Burniston Steps. As one reaches the low cliffs on either side of Burniston Steps one comes repeatedly to sections showing such similar features that a single sketch (Figure 25) can be used to illustrate them. Above the meander belt sandstones come 2 to 3 m of grey, alluvial clay with subordinate silty sandstones. One, and frequently two beds of dark, carbonaceous clay are present full of flattened plant stems. Rootlets pass down into the meander belt sandstone. Sideritisation in the clay and upper meander belt sandstone is intense, both as large concretions and as beds of sphaerosiderite. These ironstones are interpreted as evidence for the existence of ancient soil profiles (the palaeosols of Kantorowicz, 1990). Siderite in such quantities would be expected to precipitate from oxygen deficient ground water beneath peaty soils, represented here by the carbonaceous clay.

Thin alternations of sheet sandstone and silty clay follow, with the development of at least a dozen localised channels many of which were first described by Black (1928), and are known by Black's letters A to H. In almost all sections one can demonstrate that level-bedded alternations of siltstone and sandstone pass laterally into strongly cross-bedded channel sandstones, with the channels cutting through the clays and frequently resting on meander belt sandstone. The Footprint Bed is just above the horizon at which channels develop, and is succeeded locally by a thin, quasi-marine sandstone. Close to Burniston Steps the footprint sandstone forms an overhanging ledge. **Please do not hammer here.**

3C. The south end of Burniston Bay. Passing a small channel developed just above the beach 100 m south of the steps, in the southeastern corner of the bay one sees a second small channel in the base of the cliff. Above comes the Footprint Bed, and then a bed of sandstone increasing to 90 cm in thickness southeastwards. Many blocks of this sandstone have fallen onto the shore. The bed consists of a well-sorted, ripple-drift laminated, fine grained sandstone. When blocks have turned over in falling, the lower surface reveals numerous infilled burrows of the marine trace fossil *Ophiomorpha* (Livera & Leeder, 1981). However, the top surface of the bed contains numerous rootlets, thus indicating that the marine episode was very brief. At the southeastern end of the exposure, where the marine bed is wedging out, its underside reveals infilled scour channels or gutter marks running parallel to the cliff. The slightly sinuous channels are at least 7 m long, 10 cm deep and 'U' shaped. Upturned blocks on the beach show level-bedded sandstone infilling the channels. The marine bed occupies no more than 120 m of the cliff-section at this end of Burniston Bay and appears to be a lens almost certainly infilling a shallow channel scoured by a tidal surge. Thin, localised deposits of a similar nature occur elsewhere in Burniston and Scalby Bays at the same horizon.

3D. Cromer Point. At Cromer Point, Black's channel E is seen well, there being a rapid lateral transition from off-bank laminated siltstones and sandstones into massive channel sandstone.

Cloughton Wyke to Scalby Ness

Having rounded Cromer Point it is necessary to negotiate Longhorne Wyke. The cliff on the south side of this gully falls sheer into the sea for much of the tidal cycle, and **it is not possible to get round it within 3 hours either side of high tide**. One can ascend the cliff by the rough path running up the north face of the headland, or make one's way up the grassy cliff in the centre of Longhorne Wyke, rejoining the excursion at Locality 4B.

Locality 4. Scalby Bay (Scalby Formation).

South of Cromer Point, within the long stretch of Scalby Bay, there is a succession of small bays cut in the soft siltstones and clays of the Long Nab Member, with promontaries in between formed by Black's sand-filled channels projecting from the cliff (Figure 26). **Cliff falls take place regularly here, and care should be taken.**

4A. The beach and cliff south of Longhorne Wyke. As one proceeds south from Cromer Point cross-bedded meander belt sandstones are excellently displayed in the rock platform. Small-scale cross-bedding within the massive, southerly dipping beds, particularly the infilling of small chute channels by trough cross-bedding, shows that the current flow was eastwards.

On reaching the large pile of sandstone blocks marking the next channel (TA 029925), two small sandy bays are seen, with channels F and G forming promontaries. For 100 m south of the sandstone blocks, the cliff section reveals a whole series of small, sand-filled channels stacked one above the other, some choked with the carbonised remains of tree trunks, and with much slumping. This complex series of beds passes laterally into sheet sandstones and shales with occasional dinosaur footprints. Out on the rock platform the position of the meander belt is occupied by a series of almost level-bedded, ripple-marked sandstones alternating with shales containing plants. Here we have the original sediments laid down above the Moor Grit Member, which through most of the area have been reworked to form the meander belt.

4B. The rock platform northeast of Scalby Lodge. South of channel G, an excellent meander belt channel is seen in the rock platform, with a predominent cross-bedding dip to the east, and a subsidiary westerly dip. Infilled chutes show a northerly current flow. This channel cuts across a series of almost flat-lying sandbanks which gradually acquire a southerly dip southwards. At the small valley 200 m south of channel G, the sandbank nearest present high water mark displays a 10 m long trail of dinosaur footprints (Figure 26). Photographs of this locality were published by Delair and Sargeant (1985, fig. 3). The poorly sorted fluvial sand was compacted under and around the prints, which are now being revealed by the selective erosion of the overlying argillaceous sandstone.

4C. Cowlam Hole. Opposite this southernmost of the two small valleys (Figure 26), a meander belt channel makes a spectacular 180° sweep across the rock

Cloughton Wyke to Scalby Ness

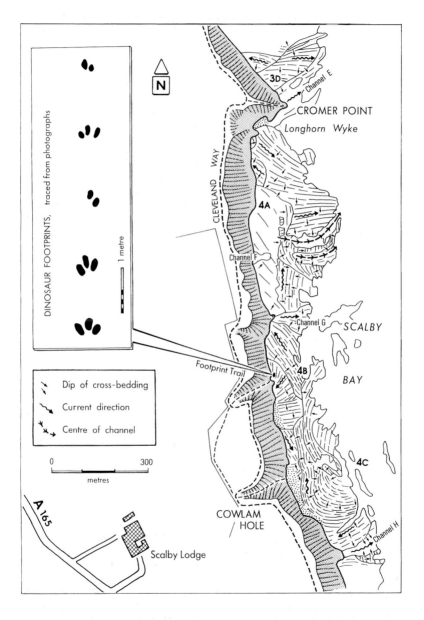

Figure 26. Map of meander belt channels, Scalby Bay. (Based on field mapping by JKW, 1969).

platform (Figure 24). Cross-bedding dips swing round from northeast through southwest to southeast. Trough cross-bedding within the chutes shows that the current flow was clockwise. Seawards, a later channel cuts across the meander and also cuts across several earlier channels to the north.

4D. Scalby Ness. Proceed now across Black's channel H into the southern end of Scalby Bay and round onto Scalby Ness (Figure 20). The gentle seaward dip carries down to sea-level Long Nab Member shales which overly the meander belt and are exposed in the base of the cliff. This is the Scalby Plant Bed, a cross-bedded, channel-fill sandstone which has clay drapes over the thinly bedded sand laminae. The clay drapes mark pauses in the current sufficient to allow plant debris to settle out. Fronds of *Ginkgo huttoni* are very common. Southwards, a series of small faults brings up the Moor Grit into the base of the cliff. As before, the top surface of the Moor Grit is rooted and deeply sideritised. If the tide is in, it may be necessary to climb the grassy cliffs here to gain access to the cliff path and to the Scalby Mills Car Park. In the season, buses travel from here to Scarborough town centre. Otherwise it may be necessary to walk to the Corner Cafe (TA 037897) to catch a bus.

ITINERARY 6

Egton Bridge and Goathland

J.E. Hemingway, revised by J.K. Wright

OS   1:25,000 Outdoor Leisure Map Sheet 27
          1:50,000 Landranger 94 Whitby
GS   1:50,000 Sheet 43 Egton

This short excursion is designed to occupy a morning or an afternoon when tidal conditions preclude shore geology. It comprises a car or minibus tour over the southern side of the Esk Valley from Egton Bridge up to Goathland (Figure 27). The itinerary is not suitable for coaches. Much of it is concerned with the effects of the last (Devensian) glaciation upon the topography and drainage pattern of the area, although visits are also made to two rock units not seen in the coastal itineraries. Walking is minimal, with the exception of Locality 8, where it is necessary to ford Eller Beck.

The region around the villages of Egton Bridge and Goathland displays most clearly the glacial phenomena consequent upon the retreat of the ice front from Cleveland to the sea. During Devensian times ice impinged on NE Yorkshire from the west, north and east. To the west, the Vale of York ice pushed south below the western escarpment, but failed to over-ride it effectively. From the northeast more vigorous ice drove inland from the North Sea over the coastline for a distance of up to 20 km. The middle of NE Yorkshire remained ice-free (Figure 5), though

Egton Bridge and Goathland

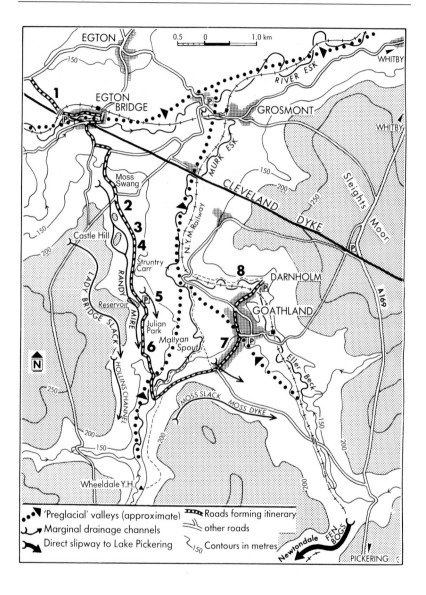

Figure 27. Map of the Egton Bridge to Goathland area (Itinerary 6). The reversal of drainage directions from pre-glacial to glacial times is indicated. Except in the river gorges, drift covers all the area below 180 m O.D.

undoubtedly snow-covered, and its drainage valleys were effectively ice-blocked. Meltwater produced during glacial retreat therefore accumulated in the valley heads until either it overflowed across confining spurs, usually (but not always) at the contact with the ice front, or passed beneath the ice in subglacial drainage channels. The recognition of this phenomenon in NE Yorkshire by P.F. Kendall (1902) and subsequent workers has resulted in this region now being regarded as classic in the demonstration of marginal and subglacial glacial drainage channels, glacial lakes and their related features and deposits.

Kendall envisaged an ice barrier blocking the Esk Valley between Egton and Goathland and creating a 17 km long Lake Eskdale. The lake would have been over 100 m deep, and water from it would have drained southwards, initially at 230 m O.D., down the west side of the ice-blocked Murk Esk valley, and southwards again through Newtondale to Lake Pickering.

Gregory (1962, 1965) has suggested that the former extent of ice cover in Eskdale was underestimated by Kendall, and that much of west and central Eskdale was under ice. The glacial drainage channels in Eskdale which Kendall described do not offer any positive evidence for the former existence of a lake. The location and morphology of these channels can be explained satisfactorily by superimposition of subglacial streams. The pattern of deglaciation must have been intricate and complex. Meltwater and depositional features show that the ice was ultimately stagnant in all parts of Eskdale. Subglacial drainage was a characteristic feature of the ice mass.

Though it is no longer thought that Lake Eskdale existed, Gregory has confirmed that a small lake did occupy the Wheeldale valley during the early stages of deglaciation, as Kendall had suggested. This lake and its associated drainage channels will be examined during the excursion. The floors of the channels are now hidden under peat, but their upper slopes are virtually unaltered in the sharpness of their incision. Two stages of formation of drainage channels are shown in Figure 27. The highest one, Lady Bird Slack and Hollins Channel, formed the first line of marginal glacial drainage channels draining down to the lake at 156 m O.D. The drainage from Lake Wheeldale was then through Moss Slack and down Newtondale.

The higher flat of Lake Wheeldale was formed at this time, and the lower one during the second stage of marginal drainage through Moss Swang and Randay Mere. During this second stage the outlet of Lake Wheeldale was through the Goathland Church Channel towards Newtondale. This lower drainage system is the one which will be examined closely during the excursion. The itinerary also points out such parts of the solid geology as merit attention.

Locality 1. Duckscar Quarry, Egton Bridge (Cleveland Dyke).

There are no problems of access to this disused roadside quarry at NZ 798053, and parking is available for several cars. The quarry face reveals a well-exposed section in a Tertiary tholeiite, the Cleveland Dyke, here 9 m wide. Tholeiite is a type of basalt, usually lacking in olivine and non-porphyritic. The Whitby Formation is the country rock; it yields abundant *Pseudomytiloides dubius* and thus is most probably at the level of the Bituminous Shales. Metamorphism is slight, but a few centimetres of baked and whitened shale may be seen welded on to the outstanding weathered walls of the dyke.

Locality 2. Moss Swang.

Return to Egton Bridge, and follow the road signposted Goathland. At the crossroads (NZ 807038) stop and observe the great, flat-floored channel of Moss Swang just west of the road. This is one of the finest of the marginal glacial drainage channels which carried water draining south. Here, both sides of the channel are cut in solid rock. Turning to the east, observe the view down lower Eskdale and across the Eskdale Dome. This structure yielded natural gas from which Whitby and district was supplied in the 1960's. Notice in particular the flat-topped feature at approximately 76 m O.D. which extends along the valley side near Newbiggen Hall (NZ 841069) for nearly 2 km. This surface, cut in boulder clay, may be traced at rather higher levels above Grosmont and is a high terrace of the late-glacial Esk graded to the 58 m sea-level.

Locality 3. Castle Hill.

At NZ 810032 park and observe the unusual pattern of channels surrounding the outlier of Castle Hill. West of Castle Hill a channel cuts about 15 m into solid rock, but hangs at its northern end in particular 15 m above the main Moss Swang channel. Kendall regarded this as indicative of the readvance of a small lobe of the ice front over the older Moss Swang channel, so that meltwaters were forced to cut a new channel which reached a depth of only 15 m before a recurrence of retreat caused its abandonment. A second interpretation is that both channels were part of the uninterrupted retreat sequence: excavation along Moss Swang and to the west of Castle Hill cut down for 15 m; a minor retreat then exposed a pre-existing gully in the eastern wall which, because of its greater depth, was followed by the melt-waters and deepened to its present form. This latter opinion is supported by the absence of glacial deposits, as well as the sharpness of the topography on the north side of Castle Hill, which would not be expected if re-advance had taken place.

The possibility of meltwaters draining through and particularly below the ice must also be considered (Gregory, 1962, 1965). Many channels undoubtedly cut by meltwaters are clearly not marginal to an ice sheet. Modern, near-stagnant ice shows that much, if not the majority, of meltwater passes though or below the ice, initially by fissures and crevasses, and not marginally round the ice edge. Many topographical features, inexplicable as marginal drainage phenomena, are clearly formed by these processes and the Castle Hill channels are most likely to be of this origin.

Locality 4. Struntry Carr (NZ 811026).

In this area the channel as such is absent. The moor edge escarpment is sharpened and the meltwaters flowing along it were contained on their eastern side by the ice wall.

Locality 5. Randay Mere (NZ 811019).

A car park is available on the eastern side of the road. Here, the meltwaters have cut a fine channel through solid rock on both sides. The channel is now used as a storage reservoir, dams being necessary at both ends as the slope of the channel floor is very gentle.

Locality 6. Julian Park (NZ 814010).

The channel lost its identity here as the waters emptied into Wheeldale Lake. The sediments of its flat floor, built up to approximately 156 m O.D., completely choked the pre-existing river valley so that post-glacial drainage followed the new line cutting the rock gorge at New Wath Scar (NZ 820006) and Hollins Wood. Here, massive sandstones and siltstones of the Saltwick Formation, with frequent plant debris, as well as the Eller Beck Formation, are exposed in the immature rock gorge. The gorge can be reached most easily at Mallyan Spout (NZ 825009), a local beauty spot signposted from the Goathland road.

Locality 7. Goathland.

Cross West Beck and continue to Goathland, noting the position of Moss Slack (intake at NZ 821001), which carried the overflow waters during the higher drainage stage along the northern edge of Two Howes Ridge from Lake Wheeldale to Newton Dale. A peat-filled depression behind Goathland Church (NZ 832011) marks the lower drainage stage along this feature. If time allows, proceed along the Pickering road for 1.5 km for a view of the intake of Newtondale, the direct glacial drainage channel which carried the meltwaters south across the unglaciated central tract to join Lake Pickering.

Locality 8. Eller Beck (Eller Beck Formation).

Proceed northwards from Goathland through Darnholm, and ford Eller Beck at NZ 835022, a small car park being available on the north bank of the river. Proceed downstream, crossing the river at a suitable point to examine the type section of the Eller Beck Formation. The following section is adapted from Fox-Strangways (1892) using the terminology of Knox (1973):

South Bay, Scarborough, Cayton Bay and Gristhorpe Bay

Eller Beck Formation

Sandstone unit:

6.	Sandstone, hard at the top, flaggy at the base, with a few impressions of *Modiolus* and *Meleagrinella*. Strong ripple marks are present, with many trace fossils.	3 to 4 m

Shale unit:

5.	Ferruginous, silty shale.	1.2 m
4.	Tough, sideritic mudstone, crowded with fossils.	0.12 m
3.	Ferruginous shale	1.5 m

Goathland ironstone unit:

2.	Sideritic mudstone, full of comminuted shells	0.35 m

Saltwick Formation

1.	Shales	seen to 0.6 m

The list of bivalves found in the ironstone beds is long: *Pholadomya, Pleuromya, Astarte, Cardinia, Nucula, Tancredia, Trigonia, Ostrea, Gervillia* and *Pinna*. The gastropods *Littorina* and *Turitella* also occur. However, much of the fauna is stunted, and the small bivalves and gastropods are preserved in dickite (a clay mineral) and poorly displayed. Downstream, massive sandstones dominate the Saltwick Formation at this locality, forming a substantial waterfall (Thomason Foss). The hillside north of Goathland is scarred by quarrying both of this sandstone and of the Cleveland Dyke, the latter no longer being exposed.

ITINERARY 7

South Bay, Scarborough, Cayton Bay and Gristhorpe Bay

J.K. Wright

OS	1:25,000 Sheet TA 08/09/18 Scarborough
	1:50,000 Landranger 101 Scarborough
GS	1:50,000 Sheet 54 Scarborough

This itinerary demonstrates Middle and Upper Jurassic sequences south of Scarborough. The route follows the beach and rock platform from Scarborough through Cornelian and Cayton Bays to Gristhorpe Bay (6 km). The going is fairly straightforward. The excursion is best done on a falling tide. Difficulties may be experienced in several places when the tide is in, though there is no danger of being cut off. In particular, the sea reaches right up to the base of the cliff at Locality 1A, and one should not rely on being able to pass this point within three

South Bay, Scarborough, Cayton Bay and Gristhorpe Bay

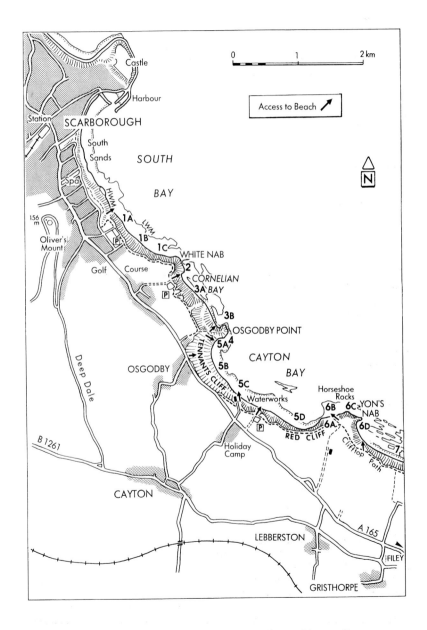

Figure 28. Map of localities in the Scarborough to Yons Nab area (Itinerary 7).

South Bay, Scarborough, Cayton Bay and Gristhorpe Bay

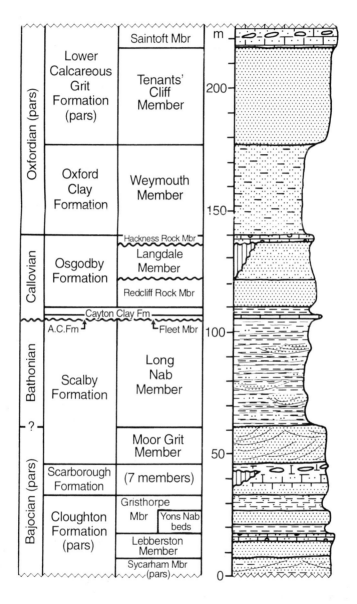

Figure 29. Simplified lithic log of the succession from South Bay to Cayton Bay. (From Rawson & Wright, 1996, fig. 13). A. C. Fm = Abbotsbury Cornbrash Formation. (Reproduced by permission of the Geological Society).

hours of high tide. High tide reaches up to the sea wall in the centre of Cayton Bay, though a detour over the cliff top path is readily available. The itinerary is designed to be carried out by leaving Scarborough on foot and returning from Cayton by bus. A regular bus service is available. Alternatively, one may proceed from Scarborough by car or minibus, parking first at Cornelian Drive car park and using the cliff top path to get to Locality 1A (Figure 28), returning to the vehicle from Locality 4, and then driving to Cayton Bay car park and joining the itinerary at Locality 5A.

Stratigraphically, the itinerary is less straightforward than that to the north of Scarborough. Several faults belonging to the Peak - Red Cliff Fault Zone (i.e. to the Peak Trough) run obliquely into the coastal area from Castle Hill southwards. As one crosses and recrosses the faults one jumps up or down the succession several times, making reference to the lithic log (Figure 29) necessary. The advantage is that one is able to see a substantial part of the NE Yorkshire Middle and Upper Jurassic successions within a short distance. Boulder clay regularly slips down over parts of the lower cliff and this means that some sections described here may not be accessible during a particular visit.

Locality 1. South Bay, Scarborough (Scarborough and Scalby Formations).

1A. Cliffs and rock platform south of the landslip. From the Spa, proceed south along the promenade just above the sea wall. At the south end of the wall, Scarborough's South Bay is dominated by the huge rampart of boulders of Scandinavian granite which has been built up to stabilise the toe of the Holbeck Hall Hotel landslip. It was in June 1993 that the upper cliff here collapsed right across the rock platform, taking the hotel with it (Back Cover). The landslip area has now been graded, drained and stabilised. Proceed along the gravel track leading across the landslip and down the concrete ramp onto the shore. The rock platform consists of the tough, sideritic White Nab Ironstone Member of the Scarborough Formation. Bioturbation is marked, with networks of *Thalassinoides* burrows in the ironstone infilled with shelly, argillaceous limestone from the overlying bed. Sideritic concretions are developed at several horizons. Bivalves are abundant, particularly *Gervillella*, *Meleagrinella* and *Pleuromya*.

Just above the base of the cliff, there is a thin representative of the fine grained, bioturbated sandstone of the Bogmire Gill Member of the Scarborough Formation, succeeded by the massive, cross laminated sandstone of the Moor Grit Member (Scalby Formation). Erosion at the base of the Moor Grit Member is very evident; scour channels infilled with clay clasts, charcoal fragments and fossil wood cut down into the Bogmire Gill Member. The Moor Grit Member is here a 6 m thick sequence of northwesterly dipping cross-bedded units produced by the gradual migration northwestwards of a substantial channel. Frequent chutes cutting through these point bar deposits have left small trough cross-stratified infills with bedding dipping in the opposite direction to the main cross-bedding.

South Bay, Scarborough, Cayton Bay and Gristhorpe Bay

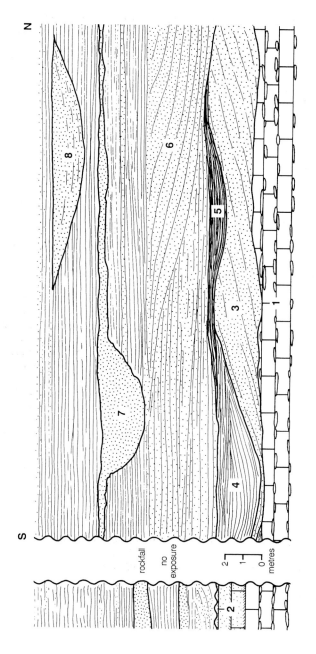

Figure 30. The Moor Grit and Long Nab Members, South Bay. A schematic diagram to illustrate the main features seen in the cliffs in the southern part of South Bay; not all these features are seen in any one section. (1) White Nab Member. (2) Bogmire Gill Member (very fine grained marine sandstone). (3) Epsilon cross-bedded sands laid down by a mature river channel migrating steadily southwards. (4) Channel infill of silt, clay and fine sand. (5) Abandoned channel infilled with carbonaceous debris. (6) Rapidly aggrading channel migrating northwards. (7) Crevasse-splay channel rapidly eroded and infilled with unbedded sand. (8) Short-lived channel crossing the alluvial flats.

South Bay, Scarborough, Cayton Bay and Gristhorpe Bay

1B. The centre of South Bay. One hundred and fifty metres south of the landslip, the Scarborough Formation is overlain by cross-bedded channel sandstones dipping southwards (Figure 30). With favourable beach conditions, scouring of the uppermost Scarborough Formation can be demonstrated, the basal part of the Moor Grit Member being coarse and ill-sorted. The persistent depositional dip in the lower cliff can be followed for several hundred metres southwards. Frequent chutes are filled with trough cross-stratified sandstone. The higher beds demonstrate deposition in a much less stable environment. Many channels are seen in section in the cliff (Figure 30). Most of the channels were infilled with sand and aggraded rapidly with little migration of the channel. Some channels were infilled with laminated silt and clay, and others became stagnant oxbow lakes infilled with plant debris and clay. The upper part of the Moor Grit Member thus formed in an unstable environment. Periodic floods eroded the underlying beds and the stream channels aggraded rapidly as they became choked with sediment. Crevasse-splaying produced sheet sands alternating with alluvial silts and clays, and the abandoned channels were filled with fine grained sediment.

1C. The south end of South Bay. The southward migration of the channel laying down the persistent, southerly dipping, cross-bedded sandstone unit can be followed towards the southern end of the bay, where these sands pass laterally into abandoned channel facies, with alternations of laminated, argillaceous siltstone and sandstone (Figure 30). South of this, erosion beneath the Scalby Formation has proceeded to a higher base level than to the north, and the interval between the White Nab Ironstone and Moor Grit Members is occupied by the quasi-marine beds poorly seen at Locality 1A. This is the Bogmire Gill Member of the Scarborough Formation (Gowland & Riding, 1991). Best seen at the far end of the sandy beach, the grey, shelly limestone described above is overlain by 2.1 m of white, level-bedded, fine grained sandstone showing delicate scour-and-fill cross-bedding. At three horizons bioturbation is well marked. Some large pedestals on the upper rock platform show beautifully the erosion of this fine grained sandstone, with hollows cut in its top surface infilled with the coarse sand of the Moor Grit Member. The Bogmire Gill Member was clearly well indurated before being eroded by the Moor Grit streams.

Eighty metres southwards, in the basal Moor Grit Member, is a bed of sideritic mudstone laid down in a small, abandoned channel, and from here the remains of the fish *Heterolepidotus* and turtle plates have been found (Woodend Museum Collection, Scarborough). The sloping upper cliff is formed of the Long Nab Member, 45 m thick, which consists chiefly of non-marine shales with occasional channel sands. These beds occupy the cliff up to the Cornbrash Formation exposed just beneath the golf course. Many blocks of Cornbrash Abbotsbury limestone containing abundant *Trigonia elongata* and *Myophorella scarburgensis* can be found on the upper beach in the centre of the bay. *Macrocephalites* can be found occasionally in these blocks.

South Bay, Scarborough, Cayton Bay and Gristhorpe Bay

Locality 2. White Nab (Scarborough and Scalby Formations).

At White Nab, a gentle anticlinal structure has brought up the Scarborough Formation sufficiently to enable a 6.5 m succession to be examined working out towards low water mark. The White Nab Ironstone Member comprises a 2.5 m succession of alternations of sideritic mudstone and calcareous, fossiliferous shale (Parsons, 1977). The best preserved fossils, including ammonites, occur in concretions in the sandy shales. The attribution of the beds beneath has proved difficult, as there is no obvious correlation with other nearby successions in the Scarborough Formation. A massive, 2 m thick sandy limestone containing *Pseudomelania* was quarried here in Victorian times as building stone for the pier at Scarborough. It may represent the Lambfold Hill Grit Member (Parsons, 1977). Shales with nodules and a band of shelly mudstone seen to a thickness of 1 m near low water mark have yielded *Stephanoceras*. This ammonite fauna is too young for these beds to be included in the Ravenscar Shale Member.

In the base of the cliff at White Nab, the White Nab Ironstone Member is succeeded by 90 cm of shelly, bioturbated, delicately laminated siltstones of the Bogmire Gill Member. These are followed by 3 m of gently cross-bedded fluvial sandstones, and then by strongly cross-bedded sandstone. The White Nab succession thus shows a steady, step by step progression from marine limestones through to strongly cross-bedded fluvial sandstones.

Locality 3. Cornelian Bay (Scalby and Osgodby Formations).

On the south side of White Nab, the Moor Grit Member strikes east-west across the rock platform as the beds take on a southerly dip. Climb over the Moor Grit outcrop, noting the beautifully displayed cross-bedding on the south side of the outcrop. The going is much more straightforward now across the sandy beaches of this pleasant little bay, more remote and less frequented by holidaymakers.

3A. The centre of Cornelian Bay. Along most of Cornelian Bay the beds are almost horizontal, with the Long Nab Member of the Scalby Formation exposed in the low cliff. The member consists predominently of shale when first seen, with thin sheets of sandstone developed at several levels, and occasional cross-sections through sand-filled channels. Progressing southwards towards the prominent channel sandstone which cuts across the beach in the centre of the bay, the relations between channel sandstones, siltstones and clays can be demonstrated in the cliff section. The clays pass laterally into alternations of clay with thin siltstones laid down during periodic flooding by the adjacent channel. Close to the wartime 'pill box', a planar-bedded, crevasse-splay sandstone cuts across the earlier beds, which are highly contorted at the junction due to water escape. The planar-bedded sandstone just above then passes laterally into the southerly dipping channel sandstone. This channel cuts right down onto the Moor Grit Member out on the rock platform. Massive, cross-bedded sandstone can be traced southwards into alternations of thick, sandy beds with laminated siltstones and sandstones.

3B. The southern end of Cornelian Bay. Some 150 m before the southern end of Cornelian Bay the western branch of the Cayton Bay Fault is crossed. The downthrow of 45 m to the east brings the Cornbrash Formation down to the beach. This is exposed just below high water mark when the base of the cliff has been cleared of boulder clay by storms. All four subdivisions of the Cornbrash (Wright, 1977) are present, with occasional *Macrocephalites* sp. There then follows the type succession of the Osgodby Formation. The three members of the formation are well developed here: the Red Cliff Rock, 3.5 m of iron-rich sandstone containing nests of fossils including numerous bivalves and *Kepplerites*, the Langdale Beds (3.8 m), bioturbated sandstone with moulds of belemnites and *Gryphaea* overlain by bioturbated silts with *Erymnoceras*, and finally the Hackness Rock (0.77 m), a sandy, chamositic limestone containing *Quenstedtoceras* and *Kosmoceras*. The overlying Oxford Clay is well displayed, and this locality was at one time considered to be the type locality for the Callovian/Oxfordian junction. The basal *scarburgense* Subzone of the Oxfordian is thin (35 cm), but yields phosphatised *Cardioceras scarburgense*. The overlying thick, silty clays of the Weymouth Member of the Oxford Clay have yielded *Cardioceras praecordatum* and *Peltoceras* (Wright, 1968).

Locality 4. Osgodby Point (Millepore bed, Lebberston Member).

The eastern branch of the Cayton Bay Fault, with an upthrow of 110 m to the east, cuts through the headland of Osgodby Point and brings the Millepore bed up to form a natural barrier protecting the headland. In fact, the Eller Beck Formation is brought up along the line of the fault in the centre of Cornelian Bay, but this exposure is only visible at very low tide (Livera & Leeder, 1981). The fault plane is exposed in the rock platform, the Hackness Rock Member and Oxford Clay Formation being faulted against poorly sorted, micaceous sandstone of the Sycarham Member. The fault plane dips at 45° to the WSW.

Proceed eastwards, keeping close to the sea below mid-tide level, over barnacle and limpet-covered boulders, where the going is easiest. Traversing the large boulders at the base of the cliff can be difficult. The Millepore bed can be examined in great detail along the numerous intersecting joint surfaces and on weathered blocks. It comprises a cross-bedded, bioclastic limestone, there being at least five courses of limestone, the cross-bedding in each having a preferential dip varying in direction from one course to another, but also varying within courses. The two highest beds have in their top surfaces extensive infilled *Thalassinoides* burrow networks suggestive of pauses in sedimentation, but the lower courses of limestone exhibit no such evidence. The Millepore bed was thus laid down in very shallow water, with strong tidal currents sweeping in the coarse shell sand and producing the marked cross-bedding.
A prominent constituent of the shell sand is the bryozoan *Haploecia [Millepora] straminea*, and this exposure should be regarded as the type locality of the Millepore bed. In the cliff above, the Yons Nab beds, which are at the base of the Gristhorpe Member, are represented by a barely marine sequence of flaggy, laminated sandstones and siltstones showing intertidal flaser structure and occasional bioturbation. They are succeeded by strongly cross-bedded sandstones.

Locality 5. Cayton Bay (Ravenscar to Corallian Groups).

5A. The northern end of Cayton Bay. Rounding Osgodby Point, the main Cayton Bay Fault is again crossed, and a small, boulder-strewn area intervenes before the sandy beach is reached. This area of rocks contains an interesting section through the Callovian strata, though sand build-up in the summer may hide the geology. The beds dip steeply northwest into the cliff, and are separated from the cliff by a small strike fault. The Cornbrash limestone forms the reefs at mid-tide level. It is fossiliferous, with bivalves and *Macrocephalites kamptus*. Cut laquered blocks show excellent bioturbation structures. The Cayton Clay Formation is sometimes covered by sand, but can yield phosphatic nodules containing the shrimp *Meyeria*, and also *Macrocephalites kamptus*, with authigenic sphalerite. In the Red Cliff Rock Member the iron-rich beds near the top have yielded well preserved keppleritid ammonites. The Hackness Rock Member yields occasional interesting perisphinctids. These latter two exposures can be hidden by shingle.

5B. Tenants' Cliff. Crossing the sands southwards now, the next stop is at the crumbling cliffs of Tenants' Cliff. Here, the Tenants' Cliff Member (Lower Calcareous Grit Formation) comprises a thick bedded, fossiliferous calcareous sandstone. Almost all the fauna has been collected from the numerous concretions exposed both in the rock platform to the north and east of the cliff and, across a small fault, in the cliff itself. Since the site was discovered early last century collectors have broken open the concretions to obtain the excellently preserved ammonite fauna of cardioceratids, perisphinctids and opeliids with additionally bivalves, brachiopods and gastropods. It is rarely worth attempting to break open a concretion unless cross sections of fossils are visible on the outside - 90% of concretions are barren.

5C. Cayton Bay waterworks. At the southeastern end of Tenants' Cliff at low tide a section in the Middle and Upper Jurassic rocks is seen dipping gently landwards (for map see Wright, 1968, fig. 9). The Scarborough Formation is exposed at very low tide on the eastern side of the Cayton Bay Fault, east of the large area of boulders opposite the waterworks. When beach conditions are good there can be seen 5 m of fine grained, argillaceous limestone and calcareous sandstone containing occasional bivalves, overlain by 1 m of massive, medium grained shelly limestone. These clearly represent the Hundale Sandstone and Spindle Thorne Limestone members. Their presence here is very significant, for they are not present only 1.5 km away at Yons Nab, almost certainly due to contemporary movement of the Red Cliff Fault (see Locality 6 below). Moving towards the waterworks, the substantial fault with a throw of 70 m is crossed, and the next beds seen are the Red Cliff Rock Member, yielding very occasional ammonites, and a thin remnant of the Langdale Member, yielding only bivalves. The Hackness Rock Member, though covered by algae and seaweed in summer, yields numerous *Quenstedtoceras* spp. and *Peltoceras* spp. The Oxford Clay is frequently hidden by beach sand, but pyritised *Cardioceras* and *Peltoceras* can be collected.

South Bay, Scarborough, Cayton Bay and Gristhorpe Bay

Figure 31. High Red Cliff and Gristhorpe Bay. (Upper) High Red Cliff, Cayton Bay (Loc. 5D): the vertical face in the lower part of the cliff is formed by the Osgodby Formation, the slopes above expose the silty Oxford Clay Formation, while the top part of the cliff is formed by the Lower Calcareous Grit Formation. (Lower) The Scarborough Formation on the north side of Gristhorpe Bay (Loc. 6D). The figure sits on the siltstones of the Helwath Beck Member. Above are about 2 m of soft, argillaceous shelly limestones. The hard band in the upper part is the White Nab Ironstone.

5D. Red Cliff. Red Cliff is an imposing sight as it is approached across the wide, sandy beach (Figures 31, 32). The Osgodby Formation sandstones form the lowest quarter of the cliff, the steep slopes above are formed of the Oxford Clay Formation, while the Lower Calcareous Grit forms the vertical face in the upper part. Beginning at the base of the succession, the very fossiliferous Abbotsbury Cornbrash Formation forms a reef across the shore beneath Red Cliff (TA 0765 8405). A thin limestone with numerous *Lopha marshii* overlies 37 cm of chamosite oolite limestone. *Rhizocorallium* burrows from the base of the latter penetrate the underlying Scalby Formation siltstones (Wright, 1977), and hint at the major non-sequence which underlies the Cornbrash here. The lower Berry Member of the Cornbrash Formation is absent throughout Yorkshire, and the Fleet Member, as seen here, is incomplete, 5 m of beds seen in inland sections being overstepped by the chamosite oolite. Both the Fleet Member and the overlying Cayton Clay Formation are sometimes exposed at the NW end of the cliff (TA 074842).

At the foot of Red Cliff the Osgodby Formation is accessible in places, **though falling shale from above makes it dangerous to work there**. The bulk of the formation here is represented by the Red Cliff Rock Member, for which Red Cliff is the type section (Page, 1989). Many fallen blocks of fine grained chamosite oolite sandstone from the upper Red Cliff Rock Member occur on the upper beach, and yield abundant bivalves and occasional ammonites, especially *Kepplerites*. The Langdale Member is absent here due to intraformational erosion (Wright, 1968). The Hackness Rock Member comprises 1-2 m of chamosite oolite limestone at the top of the Osgodby Formation, immediately beneath the Oxford Clay. It has yielded occasional *Quenstedtoceras* and *Kosmoceras*. Fallen blocks of Oxford Clay are occasionally fossiliferous with ammonites, but the blocks of Lower Calcareous Grit which litter the shore, though often riddled with *Thalassinoides* burrows, are otherwise largely barren. This is surprising considering that Tenants' Cliff with its prolific fauna is only 1 km away.

Locality 6. Yons Nab (Ravenscar Group and Red Cliff Fault).

Proceed now along the foot of the cliff, and over the undercliff by the path leading past a notice warning of the impossibility of walking all the way to Filey along the beach. Note that the undercliff becomes overgrown with bracken in summer, and care must be taken in following the path winding through this rough, boulder-strewn ground. It is sometimes easier to keep to the boulders on the rock platform.

6A. Eastern end of Red Cliff. On reaching a small gully at the eastern end of Red Cliff, note that the Red Cliff Fault runs down the gully, and that the Red Cliff Member is now at the top of the cliff on the eastern (upthrown) side of the fault (Figure 32). The throw here is about 37 m.

Yons Nab is composed of a gently, westerly dipping succession of Middle Jurassic strata lying beneath the Red Cliff Member. The outermost reef is formed of the Millepore bed, and it and the Yons Nab beds run straight across the rock platform

South Bay, Scarborough, Cayton Bay and Gristhorpe Bay

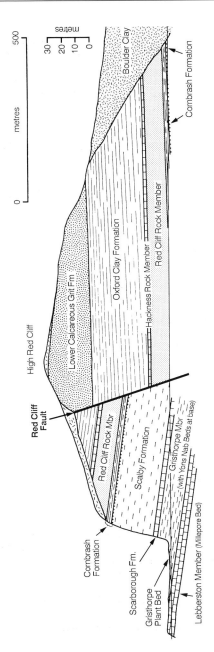

Figure 32. Cliff section at the south end of Cayton Bay.

South Bay, Scarborough, Cayton Bay and Gristhorpe Bay

to meet the fault as it runs out northwards into the sea. All the overlying beds run from the rock platform into the cliff and rise gently as one proceeds east along the Nab, and then descend back into the rock platform as one heads west into Gristhorpe Bay. The succession is thus described here as it is seen during the traverse, starting at the top (Figure 29).

6B. Northern side of Yons Nab. The first beds one comes to in the low cliff section are Moor Grit Member sandstones and siltstones. There are irregular alternations of sandstones containing much carbonised wood with laminated, silty shales. The Moor Grit Member again shows evidence of fast sedimentation, with small-scale channeling followed by rapid infilling.

Below come the 3.3 m of the Scarborough Formation (Figure 31). An upper unit consists of 2 m of soft, argillaceous, shelly limestones with a layer of concretionary ironstone (White Nab Ironstone) near the top. *Lopha* and *Meleagrinella* are abundant. Numerous small-scale faults disrupt the junction of the argillaceous limestone and the Moor Grit. Below is the Helwath Beck Member (Gowland & Riding, 1991), consisting of 1.3 m of delicately laminated siltstone with the bedding picked out by carbonaceous layers. Ripple-drift bedding and scour-and-fill structures are beautifully displayed.

The Scarborough Formation is very attenuated at Yons Nab compared with the sequence at the centre of Cayton Bay, where it is probably some 12 m thick. The Hundale Shale, Hundale Sandstone, Spindle Thorne Limestone and Ravenscar Shale Members, most of which are present in Cayton Bay, are absent at Yons Nab. The Cayton Bay exposure lies within the Peak Trough (Milsom & Rawson, 1989), a fault-bounded trough operating in Mid Jurassic times which allowed thicker sequences of strata to accumulate within the trough than on its flanks. Particularly during deposition of the Scarborough Formation, subsidence on the eastern flank of the trough, east of the Red Cliff fault, was much less than within the trough. In addition the Scalby Formation, Cornbrash Formation, Hackness Rock Member and Passage Beds Member all show some attenuation in thickness in the area east of the Red Cliff Fault. An erosive junction of White Nab Member on Helwath Beck Member is visible in Gristhorpe Bay (see below).

The silts of the Helwath Beck Member rest on 1.5 m of silty, carbonaceous shale resting on a rootlet siltstone (0.7 m). Beneath the rootlet bed is the well known Gristhorpe Plant Bed (2.5 m), consisting of thinly laminated, friable clays containing abundant plant debris and well preserved stems and leaves of Bennetitales, Ginkgoales, conifers, ferns, Pteridophytes and Caytoniales (Konijnenburg-van Cittern & Morgans, 1999). A 40 cm silty bed with roots is present near the base.

Beneath the plant bed comes a sequence of 3.7 m of marginally marine sandstones and shales typifying the Gristhorpe Member. Three beds of sandstone are present, the highest rooted to a depth of 40 to 50 cm beneath the plant bed. All the sandstones are planar bedded, delicately laminated, and bioturbated, especially the lowest one. In between are flaser bedded, intertidal, silty shales. Below the lowest sandstone comes 1 m of grey, more typical alluvial shale containing much fossil wood including large, carbonised tree branches. Working out onto the rock platform now, two beds of massive, iron-rich sandstone 90 cm and 120 cm thick are met with, separated by 25 cm of shale. The upper sandstone is bioturbated, with pyrite concretions. The lower bed contains ironstone concretions which enclose marine bivalves, and was included in the Yons Nab beds by Bate (1959).

6C. Horse Shoe Rocks. All the beds described above can be followed from the cliff onto the rock platform. The Yons Nab beds run across the rock platform just east of the Nab. They consist of 5 m of flaggy alternations of shale and siltstone with numerous small, sideritic concretions and a marine bivalve fauna. The Millepore bed forms the massive rampart at the seaward end of the rock platform. The highest 2 m consists of oolitic limestone with cross-bedding detectable beneath the barnacle-encrusted surface. Beneath, 7 m of cross-bedded sandstone is seen at very low tides, resting on fluvial sandstone of the Sycarham Member.

6D. North end of Gristhorpe Bay. The whole sequence can now be followed back in stratigraphical order into Gristhorpe Bay. Of particular note are exposures of the Scarborough Formation in the cliff and rock platform displaying an abundant bivalve fauna. Two centimetre diameter burrows infilled with bioclastic sediment descend several centimetres from this fossiliferous bed into the Helwath Beck Member siltstone. A large channel in the Moor Grit Member strongly cross-cutting level-bedded siltstones, seen at the east end of the nab, was first illustrated by Black (1928, fig. 1).

Locality 7. Gristhorpe Bay (Cornbrash, Osgodby and Oxford Clay Formations).

Proceed now to the centre of Gristhorpe Bay (TA 088837). A sequence from the Scalby Formation siltstones to the Oxford Clay Formation can be examined in the cliff, but this does involve some scrambling. The chief interest of this exposure lies in the variety of fallen blocks of Callovian and Oxfordian strata lying on the beach from which very varied faunas can be collected. The three thin limestone units of the Abbotsbury Cornbrash Formation can be distinguished: the basal, brown-weathering sideritic limestone, the middle pale grey fine grained micritic limestone containing *Trigonia* and many gastropods, and the upper bioclastic limestone containing bivalves and *Macrocephalites*. This is the best locality for Middle Callovian Langdale Member ammonites, the fallen blocks of fine to medium grained, bioturbated sandstone yielding *Erymnoceras, Perisphinctes* and *Kosmoceras grossouvrei* (Wright, 1968). The Hackness Rock Member is a pale grey limestone with scattered chamosite ooliths and yields *Kosmoceras spinosum, Quenstedtoceras* spp. and *Collotia* sp. Blocks of Oxford Clay yield well preserved if flattened *Cardioceras praecordatum* and *Parawedekindia arduennensis* (Wright, 1983).

Return now to the NW end of Gristhorpe Bay, where there is a boulder clay slope up which holidaymakers regularly tramp a path to gain easy access to the cliff top caravan site. The path here (Cleveland Way) winds its way north above Yons Nab, and then west over Red Cliff, offering splendid views of the coastal sections. An access road to houses leads to Cayton Bay car park and Cayton.

ITINERARY 8

Filey Brigg

J.K. Wright

OS   1:25,000 Sheet TA08/09/18 Scarborough
        1:50,000 Landranger 101 Scarborough
GS   1:50,000 Sheet 54 Scarborough

This is a half day excursion examining the uppermost Lower Calcareous Grit Formation (Saintoft Member) and the lower part of the Coralline Oolite Formation (Passage Beds, Hambleton Oolite and Birdsall Calcareous Grit members) well displayed in the wave-cut platform and low cliff of the Brigg. The going is fairly straightforward. Parking is available in the cliff-top car park (TA 119811).

The map (Figure 33) shows the geology of the area and the recommended stopping places. The log (Figure 34) shows the complete succession, though no more than 3 - 4 m of this are accessible at any one point as the beds dip gently in the low cliffs. The stratigraphical terminology is that of Wright (1983). Wilson (1949) published a very detailed measured section of the Coralline Oolite Formation at Filey Brigg, and this is very useful to the enthusiastic collector, although the stratigraphical terminology is very outdated. Wilson divided the succession into 34 beds, and extensive fossil lists were given for each bed. It is however difficult to match Wilson's beds precisely with those seen at the Brigg, though an attempt was made recently by Coe (1996, fig. 14). The numbers used in the log here are those of Wright (1983).

The log brings out the predominantly sandy nature of the succession at Filey Brigg. There are just three beds of standard oolitic limestone, all in the Lower Leaf of the Hambleton Oolite Member. The principle lithology at Filey Brigg is a calcareous sandstone, particularly in the Birdsall Calcareous Grit Member (beds 7 to 11). This sandstone, formerly referred to the Middle Calcareous Grit, contains an ammonite fauna identical to that found in the type quarry sections at Birdsall, near Malton. The Birdsall Member comprises a wedge of sand poured into the southern side of the Cleveland Basin during an uplift of the Market Weighton High. Oolite (Hambleton Oolite Member) continued to be deposited throughout in the northern half of the basin, but where the Birdsall Member is present the Hambleton Oolite is divided into Lower and Upper Leafs (Figure 35).

A. North side of the Brigg. Proceed along the cliff-top path to the end of the Brigg and descend to the shore. Continue over the rock platform and boulders to

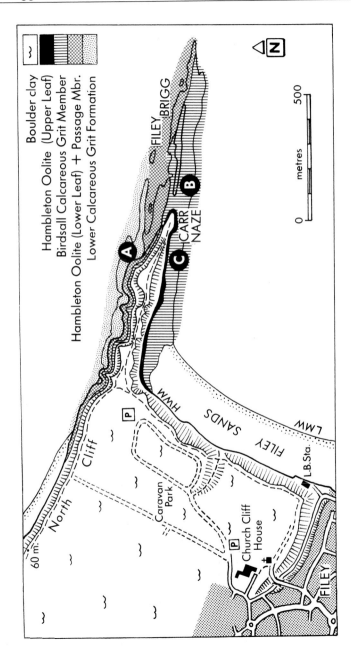

Figure 33. Map of Carr Naze and Filey Brigg (Itinerary 8)

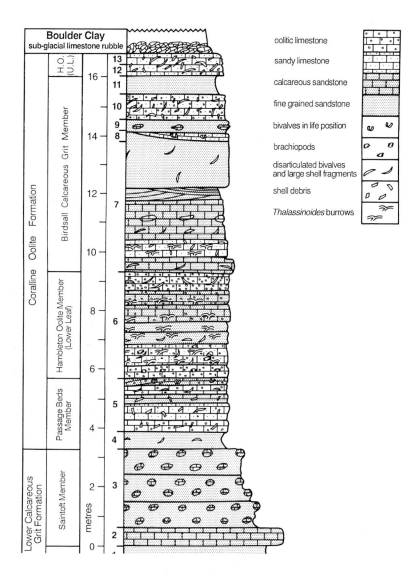

Figure 34. Lithic log of the Corallian at Filey Brigg. H.O. (U.L.) = Hambleton Oolite
Member (Upper Leaf).

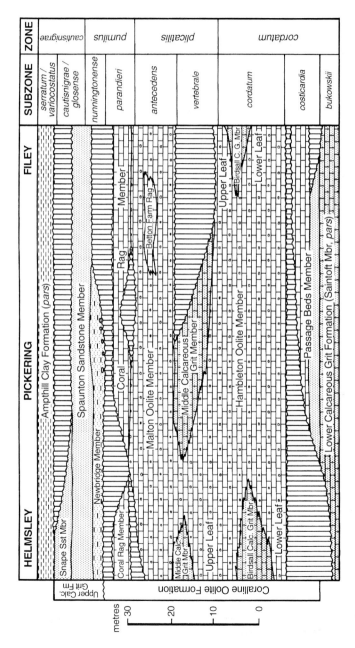

Figure 35. Schematic cross section of the Corallian rocks of the Vale of Pickering. (From Rawson & Wright, 1996, fig. 15). (Reproduced by permission of the Geological Society).

the small bay 100 m NW of the hut at the end of the path (Figure 33). The rock platform here displays the round 'cannonball' concretions so typical of the Saintoft Member of the Lower Calcareous Grit Formation. Resting on an erosion surface cut in the Saintoft Member, the lowest 0.6 m of the Passage Beds Member consist of a fine to medium grained sandstone. The sandstone is heavily bioturbated and contains *Nanogyra nana* and *Chlamys fibrosus*. Above comes the main Passage Beds limestone, 2 m of grey-weathering limestone in 5 or sometimes 6 beds (for faunal list see Wilson (1949), beds 1-8). *Nanogyra* colonies weather out, and there are many dissociated *Gervillella* valves in the upper beds, and some in life position in the top bed. Small-scale cross-bedding fills small scours, and dips to the south. The Passage Beds seem to have been deposited in a series of storm surges washing shell debris from shallow water to the northwest into the offshore shelf area to the southeast (Wright, 1992, fig. 10). There were thus brief episodes of sedimentation in an area normally accumulating little sediment. Only in the highest bed is the fauna indigenous. Compared with the 2.6 m here, 12 m of Passage Beds Member occur near Pickering (Itinerary 9).

The next 3.7 m of limestone belongs to the Lower Leaf of the Hambleton Oolite Member. A major bedding plane marks the base, above which comes the first massive bed of oolite. None of the oolites at Filey show cross-bedding and they seem to have accumulated in a fairly stable, quiet environment allowing the excellent preservation of delicate echinoids and brachiopods (for faunal list see Wilson (1949) beds 9-14 only). The quiet conditions also favoured the development of extensive networks of *Thalassinoides* burrows. The infilled burrow systems weather out in spectacular fashion in the large, fallen blocks towards the centre of the Brigg (Figure 36). The higher, sandy limestones of the Lower Leaf form the NW side of the Brigg.

B. Filey Brigg. The Brigg itself is formed of the tough, calcareous sandstones of the Birdsall Calcareous Grit Member. The full thickness is 6.8 m. Towards the base there are calcareous concretions with shelly bands containing occasional *Cardioceras* spp. Massive, occasionally cross-bedded sandstone forms the bulk of the unit with, at the top, two beds of tough, calcareous sandstone. Fossils from these beds can be collected loose from the gravel and boulders on the south side of the Brigg.

C. South side of Filey Brigg. The highest beds of the Birdsall Calcareous Grit (8 - 11) form the rock platform and lower part of the cliff here. In the corner of the bay near the sands (TA 816125), *Cardioceras persecans* can be collected from the calcareous sandstone of Bed 8. Continuing up the succession, there is a marked change in lithology from bed 9 (yellow, massive sandstone) into Bed 10 (tough, shelly limestone with many serpulae). However, there is then a return to sandy facies (Bed 11), a laminated, shelly sandstone. This contains numerous infilled *Thalassinoides* burrows descending from the shelly limestone (Bed 12) which is now, following Coe (1996), taken as the base of the Upper Leaf. The Upper Leaf of the Hambleton Oolite Member is excellently seen in a continuous section along

Filey Brigg

Figure 36. The Corallian at Filey Brigg. (Upper) General view. The ledges in the foreground form the upper part of the Lower Calcareous Grit Formation, while the prominent bedding 'plane at the foot of the ladder marks the base of the Coralline Oolite Formation. (Lower) Thalassinoides *(crustacean) burrow systems etched out on a loose block from the Lower Leaf of the Hambleton Oolite Member.*

the south side of the Brigg. It consists of tough, impure, very fossiliferous, bioclastic limestone containing well preserved bivalves and occasional *Cardioceras excavatum*, C. (*Subvertebriceras*) spp. and *Perisphinctes* sp. *Perisphinctes* is not found in the Lower Leaf and Birdsall Calcareous Grit below, these members belonging to the *cordatum* Subzone. The presence of the *Perisphinctes* and the *C. excavatum* in the highest beds suggests the presence of the *vertebrale* Subzone of the *plicatilis* Zone, normally indicative of the very highest Hambleton Oolite Member. However, the overlying beds are obscured by glacial deposits, and only 1.5 m of the Upper Leaf is seen beneath the limestone rubble at the base of the thick tills that form the bulk of the cliff here.

ITINERARY 9

Castle Hill, Scarborough and the Hackness Hills

J.K. Wright

OS   1:25,000 Outdoor Leisure Map Sheet 27, and TA08/09/18 Scarborough
           1:50,000 Landranger 100 Malton & Pickering, 101 Scarborough
GS   1:50,000 Sheets 35/44 Whitby and Scalby, 54 Scarborough

The itinerary is designed to demonstrate the relationships of sedimentary facies and the fossils contained in the varied series of limestones and sandstones which make up the major Coralline Oolite Formation of the Corallian Group in NE Yorkshire. A cross-section through the Corallian Group is given Figure 35. All of the members on the right hand side of the figure can be seen on Itinerary 9, with the exception of the Birdsall Calcareous Grit (seen at Filey Brigg, Itinerary 8), and Coral Rag members. The itinerary is arranged as a tour through the Hackness Hills (Figure 37), starting and finishing at Scarborough. The going is easy. Private transport, either car or minibus, is essential. Coaches are unsuitable.

Locality 1. Castle Hill, Scarborough (Corallian Group).

Free parking may be available at the top of Castle Road just east of St Mary's Church, though this small car park is usually full during the summer season. Alternatively, one can pay to park on the Marine Drive in the North Bay and walk up to the Castle. From St Mary's Church proceed along the footpath to the right of the road leading into Scarborough Castle and take the second path on the left through the archway leading to the North Side. If starting from the Marine Drive proceed up paths to the archway which is clearly visible. Then proceed along the rough, unmade path (which can be badly overgrown in late summer) leading eastwards below the Castle walls.

1A. The Holms. After 100 m, a beautifully weathered rock face is reached. This shows the Saintoft Member of the Lower Calcareous Grit Formation capped by

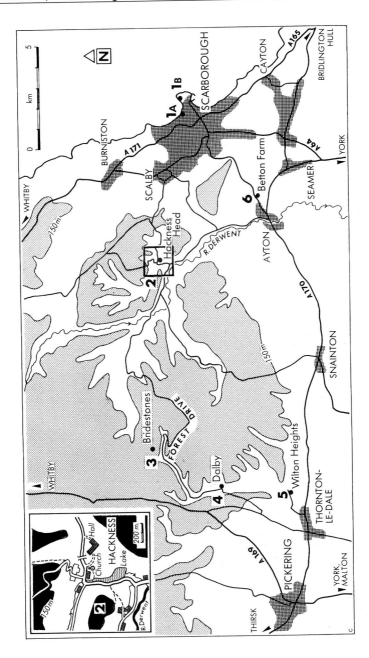

Figure 37. Map of localities in Scarborough and the Hackness Hills (Itinerary 9).

sandstone of the Passage Beds Member. There are very fine arboresques consisting of ramifying networks of infilled *Thalassinoides* burrows, and deeply weathered-out calcareous concretions. The popular name 'ball beds' is readily evident. Fallen concretions have yielded fragmentary bivalves and ammonites (Wright, 1983). A tough, calcareous sandstone marks the base of the Saintoft Member.

1B. Castle Cliff. A further 100 m to the east, a more complete section is reached, extending from the Lower Calcareous Grit Formation through the Passage Beds into the base of the Hambleton Oolite Member. A measured section was given by Wright (1983). Below the path, the Tenants' Cliff Member of the Lower Calcareous Grit Formation, though well exposed, is poorly fossiliferous. The Saintoft Member is largely hidden by grass. However, the Passage Beds Member sequence is well displayed and can be examined in detail. After an initial 1.5 m of fine to medium grained, shelly sandstone the member then comprises 7 m of alternations of laminated, silty clay with cross-bedded, shelly limestone. The juxtaposition of two such contrasting facies may be explained as follows. The area apparently lay in slightly deeper water to the east of the shallow shelf sea occupied by the Hackness coral-sponge reef (Locality 2). Silty clays were normally deposited, but cross-bedded shell sands were swept off the reef and into the Castle Hill area during storms. The dominant cross-bedding direction is thus eastwards, with subordinate westerly dips. Further up the succession the clay bands become thinner and encrusting mats of *Nanogyra nana* appear, showing that at least part of the shell fauna was indigenous rather than transported. The highest shelly grainstone limestones of the Passage Beds Member contain 10% of comminuted coral debris derived from the reef. They show markedly undulating bedding. Without the aid of thin sections is may be difficult to decide exactly where the change to fine oolite at the base of the Hambleton Oolite Member lies. Much more typical of the latter is the massive-bedded oolite exposed immediately below the castle walls, with numerous reworked *Gervillella* valves weathering out.

Locality 2. Hackness Head (Passage Beds Member).

Proceed west to the village of Hackness, 8 km from Scarborough (Figure 37). Hackness Head Quarry (SE 966904) is on private land, and permission to visit must be obtained beforehand via letter (enclosing SAE) or phone call from Mrs C. Swiers, Broxa Farm, Hackness, Scarborough, YO13 0BP, tel. 01723 882273. Park at SE 967903 in the straight stretch of road southwest of Hackness Church. Proceed up the slanting path leading westwards up the hillside, take the right fork, and immediately turn right up a steep track. Continue up by the rough, overgrown path leading into the small field at the east end of Hackness Head.

There are two small quarries here. The eastern one shows 3.7 m of the shelly, iron-rich facies of the middle Passage Beds Member. *Nanogyra nana* is abundant, with occasional *Chlamys* sp. and sponges. Some coralliferous limestone occurs at the top of this section, but it is best exposed in the western quarry, which reveals two

Castle Hill, Scarborough and the Hackness Hills

metres of white, rubbly-weathering coral-sponge limestone, the earliest known reef from the British Corallian. In the talus below the low face of the quarry can be found large colonies of *Thamnasteria arachnoides* and fragmentary *Thecosmilia annularis*. In the finer gravel are the delicate branching coral *Rhabdophyllia phillipsi* with many *Holcospongia* sp. figured by Wilson (1949, pl. 11), and also terebratulids. The reef thus consisted of discrete colonies of *Thamnasteria*, with the spaces in between occupied by sponges, brachiopods, bivalves and echinoids. Shelly lime mud was deposited between the coral colonies, much being derived from the activities of coral-boring organisms such as *Lithophaga*. New coral colonies grew on the bored remains of the old. In sheltered areas the more delicate stags horn corals *Thecosmilia* and *Rhabdophyllia* grew profusely. This was clearly a back-reef, lagoonal environment (Wright, 1992). The higher energy reef-top and reef-apron environments are not seen. The Hackness Reef as it exists today is only a remnant of the former extent of reef facies (Wright, 1992, fig. 9).

Locality 3. The Bridestones (Passage Beds Member).

This visit to the naturally weathered tors in Passage Beds Member sandstone occupies approximately one hour. From Hackness, follow the Langdale End road passing through this village and on to Bickley. Here the Forest Drive begins (a toll is currently charged). From the car park in Staindale (SE 878906) proceed NNW along the track marked 'Nature Walk', and along the path which slants NNW up through the trees.

The origin of the Bridestones has given rise to a certain amount of controversy in geographical circles. Palmer (1956) considered that during a phase of rejuvenation of the valley slopes in the last interglacial, a natural scarp formed running along the upper valley sides where the Passage Beds Member cropped out. This scarp was modified subsequently by prolonged erosion and weathering along joints to leave the pedestals or tors of calcareous sandstone remaining, marking the line where the scarp originally ran. Linton (1955), in what is a more likely explanation, held that the Bridestones could not have formed in this one-stage weathering process, and that a two-stage process was necessary. In his view, deep weathering along joints during the last interglacial left broad zones of loose, weathered rock and sand at and close to the surface. In between the weathered zones were residual, unjointed masses of unweathered bedrock. Mechanical stripping off of the weathered materials during the solifluction stages of the last glaciation left pillars of unweathered rock standing along the valley sides where weathering has been deepest and erosion most active.

The facies of the Passage Beds Member at the Bridestones is very unlike that seen at the last locality. It comprises a hard, calcareous, sparsely shelly sandstone showing marked cross-bedding with dips predominently to the west or southwest. That this sandstone formed contemporaneously with the Hackness coral-sponge reef is shown by the frequent occurrence of coral fragments in sectioned blocks of it collected from Locality 4. The quartz sand may have been brought into the area

Castle Hill, Scarborough and the Hackness Hills

by longitudinal transport along a beach barrier extending from the Market Weighton area to the south northwards into the deeper waters of the Cleveland Basin.

Locality 4. Dalby Cutting (Passage Beds).

The next locality, a roadside section (SE 854863), shows similar geological features, but there is no prohibition on collecting samples from a road-side cutting as there obviously was at the Bridestones. Proceed south down Staindale, through Dalby, and southwest up the opposite side of the valley. Near the crest of the hill, a continuous section is seen extending from the Saintoft Member of the Lower Calcareous Grit Formation through the Passage Beds Member into the basal Hambleton Oolite Member.

The Passage Beds Member is largely arenaceous but with increasing shell content upwards. Thus the lowest 3.9 m comprise fine to medium grained, calcareous sandstone, the middle 3.7 m shelly sandstone, and the upper 4.4 m are best described as a shelly, sandy limestone. The upper unit is strongly cross-bedded, the cross-sets in the main facing south, with minor north-facing cross-sets. A very shallow water near-beach environment is indicated. Coral fragments are common in this unit, and *Aspidoceras* sp. has been collected from the highest beds. The Hambleton Oolite Member rests on an erosion surface cut in the Passage Beds Member. Half a metre of oolite full of *Gervillella aviculoides* and *Chlamys fibrosus* is seen at the top of the section.

Locality 5. Wilton Heights Quarry, Thornton Dale (Hambleton Oolite Member). Continue along the Forest Drive and south to Thornton Dale. Turn left along the A170 and at the top of the hill on the outskirts of the village turn left and proceed along a narrow lane for 2 km to the quarry entrance (SE 860843). The quarry is owned by Tilcon Ltd, and permission to visit must be obtained beforehand using the following procedure: 1. A written request must be made to the Quarries Product Manager, Tilcon Ltd, P.O. Box 5, Fell Bank, Birtley, Chester-le-Street, Co. Durham DH3 2ST. This must be at least 21 days before the proposed visit. The official 'Letter of Indemnity' which will be forwarded by Tilcon must be completed and returned to the Quarries Product Manager at least seven days before the proposed visit. 3. Hard Hats and high visibility clothing must be worn at all times during the visit, which is made entirely at the visitors' risk.

Most of the inland exposures of the Coralline Oolite Formation are in large working quarries where access for parties is difficult. Unused quarries deteriorate rapidly. However, Wilton Heights Quarry still has much to offer, as it was worked until quite recently. The quarry exposes 10 m of white, creamy oolitic limestone in even-bedded units with very little sign of cross-bedding. There are abundant disarticulated bivalves, including *Gervillella aviculoides, Myophorella* sp., *Trigonia reticulata, Chlamys fibrosus, Liostrea* sp. and *Camptonectes lens*. The gastropods *Cylindrites* sp. and *Pseudomelania heddingtonensis* are also common. The occasional belemnite guard is the only indication of cephalopods. The molluscs are more common in discrete bands of well sorted oolite and appear to have accumulated by the sweeping of comparatively undamaged shell debris into deeper water during storms.

In the centre of the main north-south face a small reef-like structure (bioherm) is clearly seen in cross section. Fallen blocks reveal that the bioherm began as a colony of *Nanogyra nana* growing on a small patch of firm substrate. *Thamnasteria arachnoides* then colonised this patch, and layers of *Nanogyra* and *Thamnasteria* built up to form a solid mass of limestone up to 1 m thick. During subsequent compaction the bioherm has been pushed down into the softer, yielding oolite beneath and around it. The colonial corals are much recrystallised and are riddled with borings of *Lithophaga*. Occasional more delicate *Rhabdophyllia* also occur preserved in coarse oolite, and show the relatively quiet conditions under which the oolite accumulated. Small coral colonies and *Nanogyra* nests can be found elsewhere in the quarry. Numerous loose blocks of the Middle Calcareous Grit Member occur, but it is not seen *in situ* here. **Parts of the quarry face are crumbling and dangerous and should not be approached.**

Locality 6. Betton Farm Quarry (Malton Oolite Member with 'Coral Rag').

The quarry is situated beside the busy A170 between Ayton and Scarborough. It is necessary to park on the verge on the NW side of the road (TA 002857). Livestock are normally kept in the field in which the quarry lies, and visitors *must* obtain permission from Betton Farm, 200 m down the road, before entering the field. The quarry face has been cleaned up by English Nature, and the following section is visible:

2.	Shelly, micritic limestone containing fragmentary corals, echinoid spines, bivalves and gastropods, with large isolated masses of *Thamnasteria* up to 1 m across.	seen to 1.5 m
1.	Well- to massive-bedded, very poorly-sorted oolite containing *Bourguetia striata*	seen to 2.2 m

Bed 2 is extremely variable. Around the outside of the coral masses is a densely packed oolith-coral-shell sand with abundant abraded fragments of massive corals. In between closely-spaced coral stacks is a shelly, coralliferous, micritic limestone with abundant delicate coral fragments, including *Rhabdophyllia*, plus delicate bivalves and abraded coral fragments. The succession at Betton Farm Quarry thus represents a true reef complex, with channels choked with coral-shell sand separating large patches of coral growth. Within these patches were areas of finer, low energy sediment where fragile corals, bivalves, gastropods and echinoids could exist. It must be emphasised that the coralliferous bed here is not the true Coral Rag as surmised by most authors. Hudleston (1878) was the first to note that the characteristic Coral Rag echinoid *Cidaris florigemma* is not present here, and that

Bed 2 is simply a coralliferous facies of the Malton Oolite Member (Figure 35). This was confirmed during the cleaning up of the quarry face, when it became evident that poorly sorted oolitic limestone infilled borings and crevices in the top surfaces of the coral patches, and that there was a return to the standard Malton Oolite facies in the highest beds.

ITINERARY 10

Reighton Gap to Speeton Cliffs

P. F. Rawson

OS   1:25,000 Sheet TA 07/17 Hunmanby
        1:50,000 Landranger 101 Scarborough
GS   1:50,000 Sheet 55 Flamborough

Just north of Reighton village (TA 128757) turn off the coast road (A165) onto a minor road signposted for Reighton Sands holiday village. Follow this road until it forks at the holiday camp, then take the left branch to a small parking area (Figure 38; TA 140763). From here take the path to the beach and turn right towards the chalk cliffs in the far distance. There is a second access to the shore down a private road from the holiday camp. The shore is generally sandy, but occasionally patches are stripped off to expose either boulder clay or disturbed Kimmeridge Clay. The adjacent cliffs are of brown and reddish coloured boulder clay and show numerous landslips.

Locality 1. Middle Cliff to Speeton Beck (Kimmeridge Clay and Speeton Clay Formations).

1A. Middle Cliff. About three quarters of a kilometre from the footpath are a cluster of concrete blocks and a breakwater (Figure 38, BW1), in the vicinity of which the topmost paper shales of the Kimmeridge Clay are sometimes visible at the cliff foot or on the adjacent shore. Rarely, a band of large septarian concretions with attractive greenish-yellow calcite crystals is exposed. Flattened ammonites and small bivalves (*Lucina minuscula*) occur in both the concretions and the shales, the ammonites representing the *hudlestoni* to lower *pectinatus* Zones (Table 3). The shales are tightly folded into small, E-W trending, very angular anticlines and synclines, reflecting a Tertiary compressional phase.

From here dark grey clays appear from beneath the boulder clay in the cliff, marking the commencement of the outcrop of the Lower Cretaceous Speeton Clay Formation, which rests disconformably on the Kimmeridge Clay Formation. The Speeton Clay Formation extends along Middle and Black Cliffs for about 0.75 kilometre southeastward to Speeton Beck. The cliffs are unstable and continuously changing, so that rarely is the whole extent cleanly washed by the sea; instead there

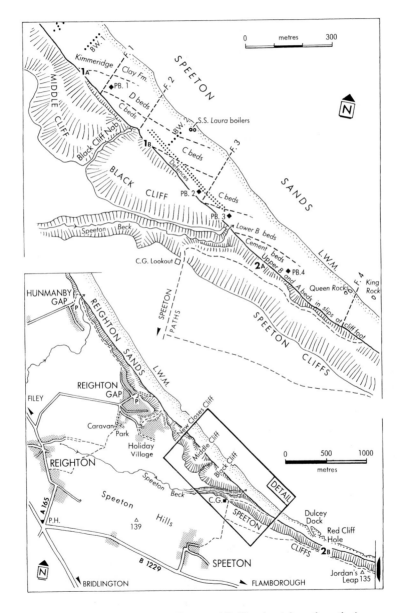

Figure 38. Map of the Speeton section (Itinerary 10). (Based mainly on the author's observations).

are often slipped clays along the cliff foot which can be very treacherous in wet weather. Conversely, patches of shingle and sand are sometimes stripped off the intertidal zone to give very clear exposures of the clays beneath. Again, the clays shows small, sometimes tight, E-W folds. The Speeton Clay Formation was divided by Lamplugh (1889) into 4 units, the A-D beds (labelled from the top downward: Table 4), characterised by abundant belemnites of alternating northern (Boreal) and southern (Tethyan) origin:

A beds - *Neohibolites* (T)
B beds - *Praeoxyteuthis*, *Aulacoteuthis* and *Oxyteuthis* (in ascending order) (B)
C beds - *Hibolites* (T)
D beds - *Acroteuthis* (B)

Finer lithological units were distinguished by Lamplugh and subsequent workers. Only the D, C and lower B beds are well exposed, and a simplified lithic log for these is given in Figure 39. Although it is difficult to follow the section in detail unless it is very cleanly exposed, there are several distinctive marker horizons which one can look for as a key to reading the sequence. The first is at the base of the clays, where a 10 cm thick phosphate nodule bed (bed E, the Coprolite Bed) with derived Kimmeridge Clay fossils marks reworking and a break in deposition over some 9 million years. This bed was mined as a source of phosphate until a major landslip closed the mines in 1869 (Lamplugh, 1889). Pit props are still uncovered occasionally at the cliff foot and help to locate the bed; where it has been mined away the immediately overlying clays are disturbed by slumping.

The commencement of deposition of the Speeton Clay Formation is the local reflection of an important sea-level rise that flushed out the whole North Sea Basin (Rawson & Riley, 1982). From then on sedimentation continued slowly, with occasional interruption, through the remainder of Early Cretaceous time.

If the Coprolite Bed is not visible the first obvious marker is usually the pale but bright, striped clay of D6. The overlying bed D5 is a brackish-water deposit which contains the primitive brachiopod *Lingula*, often preserved in its pyrite-infilled burrow. D4 marks a return to fully marine conditions and contains numerous bivalves, mainly *Astarte senecta* and the massive oyster *Exogyra latissima*. A brown-weathering silty clay with irregular concretions marks the top of D3 (D3A) and sometimes yields partially crushed large *Polyptychites*. A very distinctive band of large calcareous concretions enclosing smaller phosphatic nodules, the 'Compound Nodule Bed' (D1) is another clear marker. It reaches the shore close to a large slab of concrete that once formed the base of a Second World War pillbox (Figure 38, PB1). About a metre below D1 is a phosphatic nodule horizon (base of D2D) marking an important break in the sequence; the whole of the Upper Valanginian substage is cut out here, Lower Hauterivian clays resting on Lower Valanginian ones. Phosphatised Upper Valanginian ammonites occur among the nodules (Figure 40), together with corroded and water-worn *Acroteuthis*.

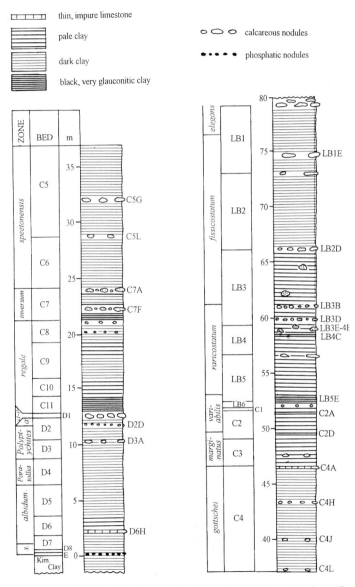

Figure 39. Simplified lithic log of the Speeton Clay Formation, D to lower B beds. In the Zone column, s = stenomphalus Zone, a = amblygonium Zone, a-n = amblygonium/noricum condensed horizon.

Reighton Gap to Speeton Cliffs

Bed D1 itself is another condensed horizon rich in fossils, including *Acroteuthis*, ammonites (*Endemoceras* and *Distoloceras* up to 0.7 m in diameter) and the 'shrimp' *Meyeria ornata*. Above, beds C11-C8 are quite fossiliferous, with attractively preserved small ammonites (including *Endemoceras regale*, *Olcostephanus* and *Parastieria peltoceroides*), *Hibolites jaculoides* and *Meyeria ornata*. A new ammonite fauna appears in C7, where *Simbirskites* (subgenus *Speetoniceras*) is common at the base and the uncoiling (heteromorph) ammonite *Aegocrioceras* (Figure 40) just above.

About 50 metres along the cliff from D1 is a thin, bright yellow sulphurous band about 3 m above the shore that forms a very clear marker zig-zagging along the remainder of Middle Cliff. This has weathered from a very thin pyrite-rich layer of volcanic origin within bed C7E and is not visible when the clay is freshly exposed on the shore. Just beneath it is bed C7F, the first of several silty, reddish weathering bands that form distinctive markers higher up the succession. The first three (C7F, C7A and C5L) can be reached via gullies in the cliff. The higher ones (C5G, C4C, C4J and C4H) are best seen on the rare occasions when the nearby beach is stripped off. Bed C7F contains common body chambers, sometimes with inner whorls, of *Aegocrioceras quadratum*, while C7A yields a Tethyan immigrant, *Crioceratites*. The clays of C6 contain small *Simbirskites*, especially near the base and top.

1B. Black Cliff. Middle Cliff terminates at a ridge (Black Cliff Ridge) that coincides closely with a fault (F2) crossing cliff and shore just before the start of a line of concrete blocks paralleling the cliffs. To the SE of the fault a low vertical cliff exposes the upper C and lowest B beds, a series of thinly bedded, cyclic units in which the 10 cm thick, intensely glauconitic bed C2D is a good marker, as are the bioturbated clays of C1 and another intensely glauconitic clay forming bed LB5E (0.46 m). Fossils are not common but the section is interesting for the occurrence of the small brachiopod *Terbratulina martiniana* in the glauconitic clays of bed C2A (see Middlemiss, 1976, p. 75).

Starting only a few metres further along Black Cliff, major landslips that over the last 15 years have obscured the immediately succeeding lower B beds have begun to clear. Hence most of the section described by Rawson and Mutterlose (1983) is becoming visible again. The most distinctive marker beds include the thin (0.23 m) very glauconitic black clay of LB4C, the calcareous silty doggers of LB3E to LB4B and the two beds of small round calcareous nodules of beds LB3D and LB3B, which are separated by about a metre of clay. These clays are not very fossiliferous, though the belemnites *Praeoxyteuthis*, *Aulacoteuthis* and *Oxyteuthis* occur in upward succession. Rare heteromorph ammonites occur, either as flattened calcareous films or more solitary fragments.

The junction between lower B and the cement beds is exposed nearly opposite a second breakwater of concrete blocks (BW2). Here, very dark, laminated, kerogen-rich shaly clays are visible just beneath a distinctive double cementstone band that

Figure 40. Remanié horizon and ammonites in the Speeton Clay. (Upper) *A major remanié horizon at the base of bed D2D is marked by a thin layer of corroded belemnites and scattered phosphatic nodules, the latter including internal moulds of ammonites. The photograph shows a well-preserved* Polyptychites *and (just beneath the clip of the biro) the alveolar view of a belemnite. The biro is 15 cm long.* (Lower) (right) *A phosphatised* Prodichotomites complanatus *(Koenen) from the remanié horizon; (left)* Aegocrioceras spathi *Rawson, a heteromorph ammonite (adjacent whorls not in contact) from bed C7A.*

marks the base of the cement beds. These clays (LB1A) are very pyritic and attractive small crystals occur in clusters. Pyritised whorl fragments of the heteromorph ammonite *Paracrioceras elegans* also occur, together with common examples of the gastropod-like serpulid tube *Rotularia*. Bed LB1A marks the top of a sequence of laminated clays (LB1A to LB1F) that can be traced across the North Sea to North Germany, where they are called the 'Blatterton' (= paper shale). They represent a brief 'anoxic' event in Early Barremian times.

Where breakwater 2 runs out to sea two ship's boilers form a distinctive landmark. They form part of the wreck of the 2089 ton Austrian steamship *Laura*, which was sailing from Newcastle to Trieste with a cargo of coke when she ran ashore in dense fog on 21 November 1897 and broke in two (Godfrey & Lassey, 1974, p.73, photos, pp. 114-115). The wreck is sometimes exhumed from the sand, when both halves of the ship can be seen at very low tides.

Beyond the basal cement beds there are extensive slipped areas of boulder clay and red chalks. The Speeton Clay reappears 30 m SE of the remains of another, tilted pillbox base (PB2), where the top C beds and lower B beds sequence appears again, repeated by fault F3. The succession is exposed along the remainder of Black Cliff. At the time of writing the section is improving and most of the sequence is exposed; all the main lower B marker beds are more clearly visible than in the preceding exposure.

Locality 2. Speeton Beck to Red Hole (Speeton, Hunstanton and Ferriby Chalk Formations).

2A. Speeton Cliffs. At Speeton Beck a footpath leads back to the holiday camp, though it is easier to return along the shore. Alternatively, one can continue southeastward to examine the Hunstanton (formerly Red Chalk) and Ferriby Formation Chalks beneath Speeton Cliffs. This second part of the itinerary can also be treated as a separate day, in which case it is possible to park near the church at Speeton village and follow the footpath from the church to the cliff top, then head down the undercliff to Speeton Beck (Figure 38).

To the SE of the Speeton Beck section, the Speeton Clay Formation is buried beneath landslipped chalk and boulder clay and has rarely been seen on the shore. Isolated small patches of the upper cement beds and upper B are sometimes uncovered at the cliff foot, all extensively disturbed by faulting or squeezing. Black pyritic clays (top upper B) are sometimes well-exposed opposite Queen Rock, yielding Late Barremian and Early Aptian ammonites and the bivalve *Grammatodon securis*. Slickensided calcite, a bed of tectonically-deformed belemnites and bedding-plane slips make the detailed sequence difficult to establish.

Further along, the higher shore is strewn with chalk boulders which makes the walking more difficult; between them, patches of red and grey calcareous clay

(A beds) are sometimes uncovered. Eventually the landslip area gives way to sheer chalk cliffs about a kilometre from Speeton Beck. Both in the cliffs and intermittently on the adjacent foreshore, the Hunstanton Formation ('Red Chalk') is exposed. The impure chalks and thin marls here are considerably thicker than the typical condensed limestone facies inland and mark a gradation towards the equivalent but generally more argillaceous Rødby Formation of the offshore area. Fossils are moderately common, especially brachiopods and species of the small belemnite *Neohibolites*.

Mitchell (1995) has divided the Hunstanton Formation at Speeton into 4 local members (as interpreted here). His paper includes a location map and detailed lithic logs. The lower two members are poorly exposed, but the overlying Dulcey Dock and Weather Castle Members are visible in the first cliff exposure, a low (possibly downfaulted) cliff face, and on the nearby foreshore.

2B. Red Cliff Hole (TA 165751) is a well-marked recess at the beginning of the high chalk cliffs. Here up to about 3.7 m of greenish-grey chalk (the 'Grey Band') overlies the Hunstanton Formation. It yields Cenomanian brachiopods, plus large pyrite crystals and marcasite. The 'Grey Band' is overlain in turn by another reddish-coloured unit, some 2-3 m thick. Note that the change in colour is sharp but cuts across the bedding irregularly - the grey colour is apparently secondary, due to reduction of iron minerals. Both the 'Grey Band' and the overlying reddish beds are usually placed in the Chalk Group (forming the base of the Ferriby Chalk Formation), but Mitchell (1995) assigned them to the top of the Hunstanton Formation, as a fifth (Red Cliff Hole) Member. Here, the former interpretation is followed.

Above the Red Cliff Hole Member, the remainder of the Ferriby Chalk Formation is represented by rubbly-bedded grey and pinkish chalks with two thicker pink bands about 7.5 m and 20.5 m above the base. The chalks here are in a griotte facies - anastomosing thin seams of marl enclosing nodules of chalk formed during an early stage of diagenesis (Jeans, 1980). Fossils are quite common though sometimes crushed - *Holaster*, *Pycnodonte*, *Aucellina* and brachiopods predominating.

Higher in the cliff, and inaccessible at this point, the Plenus Marl at the base of the overlying Welton Formation is visible; it lies about 44 m above the base of the Ferriby Formation.

The visitor should not walk beyond Red Hole as the sections are dangerous and the tide reaches the cliff foot in places. It is equally dangerous to scramble up the grassy slopes to reach higher beds.

Thornwick Bay and North Landing, Flamborough

ITINERARY 11

Thornwick Bay and North Landing, Flamborough

P.F Rawson and F. Whitham

OS	1:25,000 Sheet TA 26/27 Flamborough
	1:50,000 Landranger 101 Scarborough
GS	1:50,000 Sheet 55 Flamborough

The localities described in itineraries 11 to 13 lie in the area of the Flamborough Headland Heritage Coast. When approaching sections visitors are asked to keep to the marked paths. Further information on the Heritage Coast is available at the Heritage Centre at South Landing ravine (Itinerary 13).

In the Flamborough area the coastline is deeply eroded from Thornwick Bay to Flamborough Head and there are several small bays which contain magnificent arches, caves and sea stacks cut into hard chalk - so hard that it has been used as a building stone and can be seen in some of the older buildings in the area, including the 17th century lighthouse. At low tide some of the caves and arches provide access to adjacent coves, from which there is no escape when the tide turns. **It is highly dangerous to stray beyond the confines of the bays described here**.

Throughout the Flamborough area the Chalk is overlain by a thick blanket of boulder clay, and it is the contrast between the two that causes such a marked change in slope half to three quarters of the way up the cliffs. In places, downwash from the clay smears the chalk while fallen lumps are soon broken up by the sea to release the enclosed erratic rocks and fossils. Hence, although the local beach shingle is predominantly of local flint and chalk it contains numerous exotic pebbles, including small carnelians. Spectacularly large boulders of various types, including Shap Granite, are scattered over the beaches.

Locality 1. Thornwick Bay (Welton and Burnham Chalk formations).

From Flamborough village take the B1255 towards North Landing, turning immediately before 'The Viking Hotel' (Figure 41) onto a track signposted 'Thornwick Bay' for almost a kilometre until the track terminates at a parking area opposite the Thornwick Cafe. With care a coach can drive here. A footpath in front of the cafe leads to Thornwick Nab; the path soon forks, the left fork leading into Little Thornwick Bay and the right fork into Great Thornwick Bay.

In both bays the chalk is very sparsely fossiliferous and belongs almost wholly to the *Terebratulina lata* Zone of the Turonian. The exposures are of interest primarily to show how this single, ill-defined Chalk zone can be subdivided lithologically. The sequence embraces the upper half of the Welton Chalk Formation and the base of the overlying Burnham Formation, and contains a number of named marl and

Thornwick Bay and North Landing, Flamborough

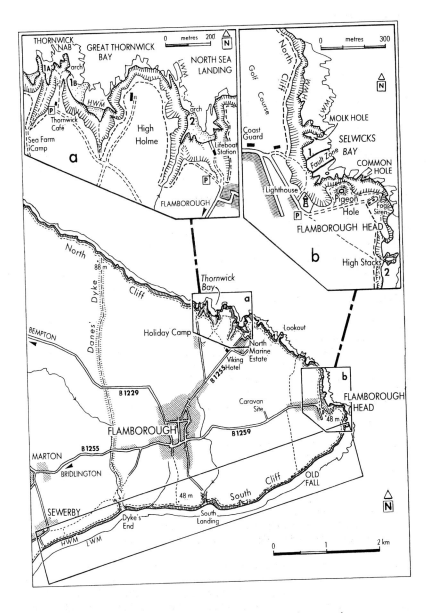

41. *Locality map of the Flamborough area (Itineraries 11-13). The rectangle extending from Sewerby to Flamborough Head shows the area of Figure 46.*

flint bands (Figure 42). The sediments accumulated along the southern margin of the Cleveland Basin, within the Howardian-Flamborough Fault Belt, and are almost 10 metres thicker than in correlative sections on the northern part of the East Midlands Shelf.

IA. Little Thornwick Bay. The lowest beds are visible on the north side of the bay (Figure 43, and Front Cover), where four deeply eroded, narrow clefts near low water mark (the lowest at the foot of the arch on the seaward side) represent the individual marl bands of the Barton Marls. The Ferruginous Flint about 3 metres higher is a prominent 15 cm thick tabular, carious flint with red-weathering patches. This bed can be traced on both sides of the bay and round Thornwick Nab into Great Thornwick Bay, forming one of the best marker bands. *Inoceramus lamarcki* occurs 2.75 m below this band. A second good marker is a 2-4 cm thick marl, the Melton Boss Marl, which forms a prominent line in the cliff at the head of Little Thornwick Bay.

1B. Great Thornwick Bay. From Little Thornwick return up the short cliff path and cross into Great Thornwick Bay. On either side of the path as it reaches the beach the highest flint band seen is the band of semi-tabular flints 5.4 m above the Ferruginous Flint. The latter is readily visible round the corner to the left, where it rises from near shore level to form the roof of the arch at Thornwick Nab (Figure 43). From here the succession can be traced across the scars to the southern and eastern sides of the bay. In the cliff on the southern side the lowest flint band is a prominent grey tabular flint, the Deepdale Flint, which rises westward from the foot of the cliff. Above are two deeply weathered notches formed by the Deepdale Lower and Upper Marls, and the sequence can be traced upward to the Ravendale and Triple Tabular flint bands. These form equally clear markers at the head of the bay on the eastern cliff. The suggested boundary of the *Terebratulina lata* and *Sternotaxis plana* zones is at the base of the 50 cm unit of thinly-bedded chalks directly below the Ravendale Flint, where the first *S. plana* occur. *Gibbithyris semiglobosa* is present just above the flint.

Once the Ravendale and Triple Tabular flints have been identified it is easy to follow the succession downwards along the eastern cliff to the Melton Ross Marl, which forms a deep cleft in the cliff foot at low water mark.

Locality 2. North Landing (Welton and Burnham Chalk formations).

From Thornwick Bay either walk along the cliff top path eastwards or drive back to the B1255 and turn left to North Landing (Figure 41). The road terminates in a large car and coach park. From there walk down the cliff road adjacent to the cafe and pub. At the head of the bay on the left hand (western) side is a slight embayment and cave in the Chalk. A prominent ledge rising eastwards from beach level marks the position of a useful marker bed, the Ulceby Marl. A second marker horizon can be picked up about halfway along the western side of the Landing, at a conspicuous marine arch. Here the Ravendale Flint is about 2 metres above shore

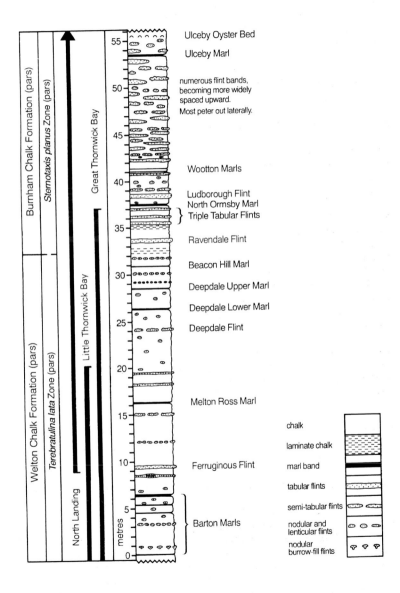

Figure 42. Lithic log of the Chalk at Thornwick Bay and North Landing. (Based on the authors' observations).

Thornwick Bay and North Landing, Flamborough

Figure 43. The Chalk at Thornwick Bay. (Upper) Little Thornwick Bay: the Barton Marls occur at the foot of the cliff where the waves are breaking. The Ferruginous Flint (FF) is 3 metres above, while the Melton Ross Marl (MR) forms a notch higher in the cliff. (Lower) Thornwick Nab: the Ferruginous Flint (FF) is the prominent band half-way up the cliff.

level, and just above it are the Triple Tabular Flint bands, with the prominent Ludborough Flint about half way up the inside walls of the arch. At the northwestern extremity of the Landing the remains of a ship's boilers lie in a deep cleft; a prominent rusty-brown flint band adjacent to them is the Ferruginous Flint. These three marker levels allow the whole succession (Figure 42) to be followed.

On the eastern side of the Landing the Beacon Hill Marl lies just above low water. A little higher in the sequence the thickest (20 cm) tabular flint, the Ludborough Flint, cuts across the mouth of Robin Lythes Hole, which leads into a magnificent cavern with another exit onto East Scar. The Ulceby Marl again forms a ledge, which descends to the shore in the cliff immediately adjacent to the lifeboat slipway.

Fossils are not common through most of the succession, but *Sternotaxis planus* occurs in the upper beds (from just below the Ravendale Flint). About 2 m above the Ulceby Marl is the Ulceby Oyster Bed, here about a 20 cm thick band of chalk with scattered oysters (*Pycnodonte vesicularis*) and occasional brachiopods.

Both this and the following itinerary occupy less than a full day but cannot be combined safely because by the time one is finished the tide will normally have risen too much for the other. Itinerary 14 provides an interesting 'filler' to complete the day.

ITINERARY 12

Flamborough Head

I.C. Starmer and F. Whitham

OS   1:25,000 Sheet TA 26/27 Flamborough, or
             1:50,000 Landranger 101 Scarborough
GS   1:50,000 Sheet 55 Flamborough

Locality 1. Selwicks Bay (structures in Chalk).

From Flamborough village follow the B1259 to Flamborough Head, where there is a large car park and cafe adjacent to the lighthouse (Figure 41). Opposite the cafe there is a good view of Selwicks Bay. Here the chalk cliffs and foreshore are formed by the flint-bearing Burnham Chalk Formation, overlain by the flintless Flamborough Chalk Formation. The flinty chalk is referred to the lower *Hagenowia rostrata* Zone and the flintless chalk to the upper part of the same zone. Fossils are uncommon but occasional examples of *Gonioteuthis westfalica*, *Echinocorys* sp., *Porosphaera globularis*, small brachiopods and fragmented inoceramids are found. However, the main feature of geological interest is a zone of intense deformation running E-W through the bay, which represents part of

Flamborough Head

the Howardian-Flamborough Fault Belt (Figure 2). The zone shows a clear structural sequence of N-S compression (forming E-W folds and thrusts) followed by N-S tension (producing E-W striking extensional faults), both phases being related to the Tertiary Alpine Orogeny. The structure has been described in detail by Starmer (1995a).

The bay is best investigated on a falling tide. From the cliff top, the view of the intertidal foreshore shows that it is a gentle, E-W syncline, with rocks in the south dipping gently north and those in the north dipping gently south, around a hinge which is usually visible at the edge of the beach (Figure 44). Fractures represent later extensional faults which cut the synclinal structure, illustrating the sequence of N-S compression followed by N-S tension.

A path to the left of the lighthouse gate leads down the West Cliff to Selwicks Bay. On either side of the path, a variety of lime-loving flowers, including orchids, can be seen on the boulder clay slopes.

Viewing the cliffs from the beach, the sharpest features seen are the late extensional faults, striking E-W, but varying from steeply to gently dipping, with the upper sides ('hanging walls') moving downwards. The movements can be determined from slickenlines on the fault surfaces.

Starting in the south of West Cliff, the 5 m wide frontal fault zone (Figure 45) is a series of sub-vertical E-W faults causing strong brecciation. In the cliffs, the northward downthrow across the zone can be deduced from the position of the top observable flint layer (of the Burnham Chalk Formation): this is near the top of the cliffs on the southern side of the zone and about 2 m above the beach on its northern side.

To the north of the frontal zone, subhorizontal to gently dipping extensional faults extend northwards to the new steps, where a steep extensional fault curves at beach level to dip more gently northwards beneath the cliff (i.e. it is a 'listric' fault - Figure 45). On its northern side, in its 'hanging wall', the listric fault has cut earlier E-W folds and south-directed thrusts in a sheet which is limited at the top by a second, north-dipping listric fault. Northwards, the sheet of folds and thrusts disappears under the beach and the extensional faults become south-dipping along the rest of West Cliff: in other words, the north-dipping fan is replaced northwards by a south-dipping counter fan, in a similar way to structural developments in the North Sea.

About 35 to 40m north of where the thrust and E-W folds disappear beneath the beach, they reappear again. This effect results from their gradual upthrow northwards on the 'footwalls' (undersides) of the later counter fan extensional faults, graphically illustrating the sequence of E-W folding and thrusting followed by extensional faulting. At the northern end of West Cliff, the features of the North Cliff start to dominate: these are NNE-SSW and NNW-SSE extensional faults, commonly forming crossing conjugate pairs.

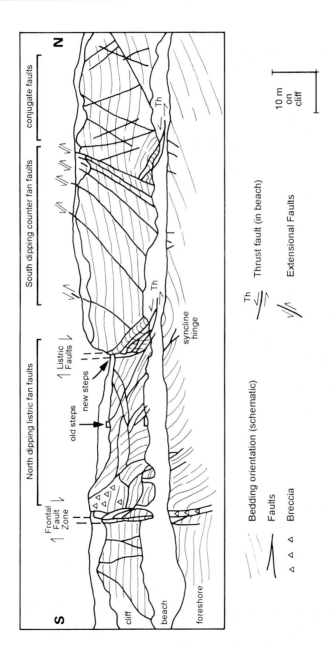

Figure 44. Structures in the Chalk, West Cliff, Selwicks Bay.

Flamborough Head

Figure 45. West Cliff, Selwicks Bay, looking due west. (Upper) Small bluff with vertical Frontal Fault Zone on left (south) edge, sub-horizontal beds across the front, and steep northward-dipping beds and listric faults on the right (north) edge. (Lower) Near the new steps, at the left (south) end, a listric fault curves north round the base of the main cliff beneath a triangular zone containing older thrusts. Above and to the right (north), another north-dipping listric fault is succeeded by south-dipping counter fan faults. In the foreground, foreshore rocks dip around the syncline hinge at the left (south) edge of the photo.

Flamborough Head

The structure in West Cliff is not concordant with that in the foreshore beneath (Figure 44), because of the thrust between them, beneath the beach. Considering the structures, the total downthrow across the whole Selwicks Bay zone is at least 18 m to the north.

At the northeast corner of the bay, a large re-entrant in North Cliff is called the Molk Hole and leads to several small caves and two spectacular arches. At the Molk Hole entrance, at the foot of the cliff, the highest flint band (the High Stacks Flint) of the Yorkshire Chalk is exposed, marking the top of the Burnham Formation. **This location should be investigated only on a falling tide.**

The South Cliff of Selwicks Bay forms the northern side of Flamborough Head: it is south of the main zone of deformation and consequently faulting is less intense. Small embayments represent collapsed blow holes (note the concave chalk faces). The solitary sea stack is locally called 'Adam'; its former partner ('Eve') on the opposite side of the bay (outboard from the Molk Hole) was illustrated by Lamplugh (1896, plate 31), but has since been eroded away.The southern side of Flamborough Head is accessed by returning up the steps and walking around the lighthouse to the track leading to the Fog Siren (Figure 41).

Locality 2. High Stacks (Flamborough Chalk Formation).

From the Fog Siren, follow the cliff top path southeastwards to TA 257704, where a track leads to the shore at High Stacks, a small, clay- and gravel-capped promontory of chalk. West from here, along the north side of Bridlington Bay to Sewerby Steps (a distance of about 6.5 km: Figure 46), a continuous 167 m succession of chalk represents all but the highest part of the Flamborough Formation. The sequence generally youngs westwards, although locally the gentle dips (0-15°) vary in direction, because of an underlying structure of gentle domes and basins on all scales, formed by the interaction of E-W and N-S folding: however, in the western part of the section, the dips are dominantly southwestwards.

There are few distinctive lithological markers, but some of the more prominent, thicker marls can be used to locate zonal boundaries (Whitham, 1993). The cliff section from High Stacks to the next access point at South Landing (about 3 km westwards) exposes the lowest part of the formation (lower part of the upper *Hagenowia rostrata* Zone), showing about 26 m of very hard, massive white chalk with a series of thin marls which increase in frequency up the succession to form a thinner-bedded sequence near South Landing.

On the shore behind High Stacks, the top flint layer of the Burnham Chalk Formation is visible, whilst a deep cleft 1.5 m above the foot of the stack represents an etched-out 2 cm thick marl, lying about 3.5 m above the base of the flintless Flamborough Chalk Formation. Most of the chalk shows little lithological variation: it dips around 10° W from High Stacks to Old Fall (about 1 km) and then

South Landing to Sewerby Steps and Sewerby Buried Cliff

becomes horizontal for about 1.5 km further west, to within 400 m of South Landing, where the low angle dips vary in direction, bringing a 1-3 cm marker marl close to shore level near the ravine.

Fossils are fairly scarce in the main part of the section, but are more common in a 1.5 m thick bed occupying the lower part of the cliff for over 2 km, equidistant between High Stacks and South Landing: this bed contains the tiny echinoid *Hagenowia blackmorei* (formerly misidentified as the larger index species *H. rostrata*, which is confined to the lower *rostrata* Zone), *Gonioteuthis westfalica*, *Orbirhynchia pisiformis*, *Porosphaera globularis*, corals and echinoid spines. In the remainder of the chalk, there are isolated occurrences of *Echinocorys* sp., fragmented inoceramids and sponges, the last found more frequently towards the end of the section. Large ammonites (? *Parapuzosia* sp.) have been recorded from South Landing. *Hagenowia blackmorei* is confined to to about 4 m of accessible chalk (some 22 m above the base of the formation) on the east side of South Landing: it also occurs on the west side, where a further 3.5 to 4 m of higher beds containing this echinoid are brought down to shore level by the southwesterly dip (see Itinerary 13).

On a falling tide only, it is possible to proceed along the shore from High Stacks to South Landing, returning via Flamborough. However, as the section is almost along the strike, it is best to return from Old Fall to High Stacks and Flamborough Head, noting the large erratic boulders, including one of Shap Granite about 1 m across.

ITINERARY 13

South Landing to Sewerby Steps

F. Whitham

and Sewerby Buried Cliff

P. F. Rawson

OS   1:25,000 Sheet TA 26/27 Flamborough
            1:50,000 Landranger 101 Scarborough
GS   1:50,000 Sheet 65 Bridlington

Starting at Flamborough village take a minor road, signposted 'South Landing', from the crossroads at TA 228702 (Figure 41). From the Heritage Centre at the car park a path leads down a ravine to the shore (Figure 46). On both sides of the Landing drift deposits mark a glacial melt-water channel cut through the chalk; the ravine follows this channel. A few years ago a storm cleared the beach in line with the ravine to reveal a chalk sequence distorted by folding or faulting, probably

South Landing to Sewerby Steps and Sewerby Buried Cliff

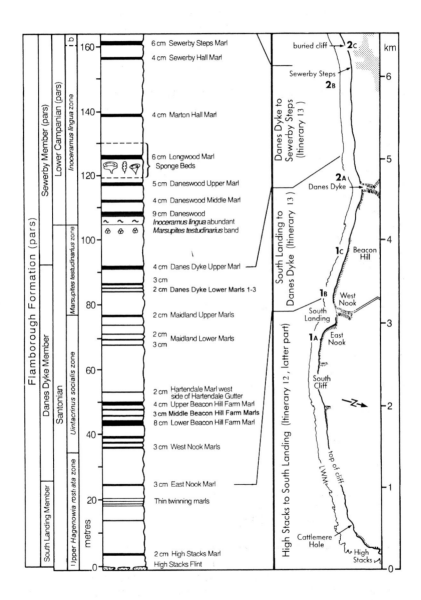

Figure 46. Lithic log of the Chalk from High Stacks to Sewerby Steps, with localities.
(Based on data in Whitham, 1993; Mitchell, 1994).

reflecting another deep-seated structure in the Howardian-Flamborough Fault Belt. This faulted ground may have formed a line of weakness exploited by the glacial melt-waters.

Locality 1. South Landing to Dane's Dyke (Flamborough Formation).

1A. East Nook. To the east (left) of the Landing are exposed the highest beds described in Itinerary 12, which may be examined if not seen on the previous walk. After about 400 m the same sequence of beds as those observed at Old Fall appear. Return to the Landing.

The walk from South Landing westward to Sewerby Steps (TA 202686) is approximately 3 km and exposes about 138 m of the Flamborough Formation sequence, from the higher part of the upper *Hagenowia rostrata* Zone (c. 13 m) through the whole of the *Uintacrinus socialis* (39 m) and *Marsupites testudinarius* (26 m) Zones to the *Inoceramus lingua* Zone (just over 60 m exposed). Halfway along the section is the seaward end of Danes Dyke which is the only other exit from the beach before Sewerby. Care must be taken as high tide reaches the base of the cliffs in a number of places.

1B. West Nook. In the foot of the cliffs on the SW side of the Landing the bed containing *Hagenowia blackmorei* can be traced for about 100 m before dipping below beach level and provides a link with the last locality of Itinerary 12. This species appears to be confined to beds within an 8 m sequence spanning the ravine and is fairly rare outside this horizon. A few thin occurrences are recorded elsewhere in the *rostrata* Zone, and there are isolated examples in the lower *Uintacrinus socialis* Zone and the *Inoceramus lingua* Zone. The remainder of the fauna in this part of the flintless *rostrata* chalk is restricted to occasional brachiopods, fragmented inoceramid shells, thick shelled *Echinocorys* sp., *Gonioteuthis westfalica granulata*, *Actinocamax verus*, and sponges (including *Amphithelion*, small varieties of *Laosciadia plana*, *Siphonia koenigi*, *Stichophyma tumidum* and abundant *Porosphaera globularis*).

1C. Beacon Hill. About 360 m from South Landing the boundary between the *H. rostrata* and *Uintacrinus socialis* Zones is marked by the first appearance of the zonal index in a bed of chalk approximately 4 m below the lowest West Nook Marl 1 (Figure 46). The overlying Beacon Hill Farm Marls 1-4 lie below Beacon Hill. The lower part of the *socialis* Zone comprises hard and soft chalks with thinner bedding and a few stylolitic horizons, while the higher part reverts back to more massive bedding. Stylolites are complex zig-zag contacts formed by loading and solution processes. A number of minor faults dissect the succession and several rock falls have taken place, the most massive one occurring about 200 m east of Hartendale

Gutter (a sewage discharge outlet), obscuring a large part of the cliff.
In the past it has been said that this part of the coastal sequence is one of the very
few areas in England to yield complete cups of *Uintacrinus socialis*. It is now
almost impossible to find complete specimens in the lower, accessible parts of the
cliffs, but isolated plates are common and at some horizons small groups of plates
occur possibly all forming part of the same individual. Other fossils include
fragmented inoceramids, *Echinocorys* sp., *Orbirhynchia pisiformis*, *Pseudoperna
boucheroni*, *Parasmilia* sp. and sponges belonging to the same group as listed for
the previous zone. Belemnites of the *Gonioteuthis granulata* lineage appear to be
less common and the occurrence of *Uintacrinus socialis* plates diminishes in the
higher beds, being very rare in the highest 3 m of the zone.

Rare isolated plates of the zonal species *Marsupites testudinarius* occur at and
above the 2 cm thick Maidlands Upper Marl, approximately 220 m from Danes
Dyke. This horizon marks the base of the *testudinarius* Zone, which reaches its
maximum thickness in this area. Massive bedding continues upward from the
higher part of the preceding zone but the chalk becomes softer. The lowest 15 m of
the zone occur in the cliff up to Danes Dyke, but *Marsupites* plates and other
fossils are very rare here.

It is possible to return up the cliff at Danes Dyke, following a footpath inland to
Flamborough village.

Locality 2. Dane's Dyke to Sewerby Steps (Flamborough Formation).

2A. Dane's Dyke cuts into *testudinarius* Zone chalks. The seaward end forms part
of an interglacial meltwater channel partly filled with drift which was re-excavated
during the Bronze Age to form part of an entrenchment cutting across Flamborough
Head. Faulting has been observed in the Chalk here when storms have cleared part
of the beach (R. Myerscough, personal communication). The distance from here to
Sewerby is about 1.5 km and the southwesterly dip exposes the remaining 11 m of
Marsupites chalk and just over 60 m of *Inoceramus lingua* Zone chalk of which the
highest 3 m above Sewerby Steps is assigned to the *Discoscaphites binodosus*
Subzone.

Scars on the beach at the SW side of the dyke contain abundant *Marsupites* plates.
In the cliff a 4 cm marl (Upper Danes Dyke Marl) can be correlated with the
eastern side and marks a lithological change from more massive chalks to thinner
bedded sequences parted by many thin marls. About 100 m along the section
Marsupites plates become extremely common and complete calyces (cups) are
found. This flood of the zonal species is spread over about 5 m of chalk in the
middle part of the zone and it then dies out close to the upper boundary about 200
m SW of the dyke. Note the stylolitic horizons along this section.

Other species to be found in the remaining part of the zone include *Acutostrea
boucheroni* (in bands), *Orbirhynchia pisiformis*, occasional specimens of
Echinocorys sp., varieties of *Ventriculites*, *Porosphaera globularis* and other sponges
often preserved as oxide films. Large examples of *Gonioteuthis granulata* occur.

South Landing to Sewerby Steps and Sewerby Buried Cliff

About 2 m above the last appearance of *Marsupites*, and near to four seaweed-covered calcrete blocks (first noted by Rowe, 1904), the base of the *Inoceramus lingua* Zone is marked by a profusion of fragmented shells of the zonal species. This horizon also marks the boundary of the Santonian and Campanian stages. Chalk of the *lingua* Zone is for the most part fairly hard with some massive bedding interspersed with a series of thinly bedded horizons. Stylolitic surfaces are less frequent than in the previous zone. Fossils are common at some horizons with *Inoceramus lingua* the dominant bivalve while rare examples of *Sphenoceramus pinniformis* occur. Sponges are far more common in the *lingua* Zone than elsewhere, with the best developed concentration of hexactinellid and lithistid sponges occurring in the famous Flamborough Sponge Beds, which consist of just over 10 m of chalk, the basal beds lying some 15.5 m above the base of the zone. The more shallow dip of the strata where the Sponge Beds reach the shore provides a continuous exposure on the beach scars for a considerable distance, commencing about 350 m from Danes Dyke; the main exposure lies nearer to this ravine than to Sewerby.

Many fine sponges occur in both cliff and scars, including *Pachinion scriptum*, *Stichophyma tumidum*, varieties of *Laosciadia plana*, *Siphonia koenegi*, *Rhizopoterion cribosum* , *Amphithelion (Verruculina) sp.*, *Wollemania laevis*, *Sporadoscinia strips*, *Leiostracosia punctata* and *Porosphaera globularis*. Also occurring in the Sponge Beds are very large *Echinocorys* (up to 80 mm long), *Inoceramus lingua* and *Sphenoceramus pinniformis*, with rare *Gonioteuthis granulata*. The top of the Sponge Beds is marked by three thinly bedded 20 cm chalk horizons spread over 1.5 m, with the intervening beds containing abundant *Pseudoperna boucheroni*.

2B. Sewerby Steps. Above the Sponge Beds, towards Sewerby Steps, the more massive bedded chalk becomes less fossiliferous, with sporadic occurrences of *Echinocorys*, sponges, fragmented inoceramids and shell debris. Other species recorded in the *lingua* Zone here include a band of *Offaster pilula*, *Hagenowia* sp., large and rounded forms of *Cardiotaxis*, *Hypoxytoma tenuicostata*, *Orbirhynchia* sp. and the rare ammonites *Hauericeras pseudogardeni* and *Scaphites* sp. Echinoid spines and asteroid plates are common in the lower half of the zone. *Discoscaphites binodosus* occurs in the highest 3 m of chalk, above the steps.

Locality 3. Sewerby Buried Cliff (Pleistocene features).

About 300 m SSW of Sewerby Steps is the buried cliff section described in the GA Guide to Hull (Penny, in Bisat *et al.*, 1962, p. 18). Here, the modern cliff face shows the Chalk terminating abruptly against sands, shingle and boulder clay (Figure 47). The interface marks a Pleistocene chalk cliff which runs slightly obliquely to the modern cliff and can be traced for at least 50 metres before disappearing completely behind the glacial deposits. The buried cliff then strikes inland to run along the dip slope of the Chalk Wolds to the Humber (where it is visible at Hessle) and on into Lincolnshire. It is an interesting and important

South Landing to Sewerby Steps and Sewerby Buried Cliff

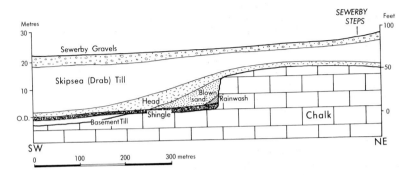

Figure 47. Diagrammatic section of the buried cliff at Sewerby. (Modified from Catt & Penny, 1966, pl. 24).

feature in the glacial chronology of the area (Catt & Penny, 1966). At the foot of the buried cliff is an interglacial shingle beach ('Sewerby Raised Beach'), about 1 metre above the modern beach level and resting on a planed surface of Basement Till, though the contact is only seen on the rare occasions when storms have stripped off the modern beach. The raised beach contains vertebrate remains indicative of the Last (Ipswichian) Interglacial, including the straight-tusked elephant (*Palaeoloxodon antiquus*), the narrow-nosed rhinoceras (*Dicerorhinus hemitoethus*) and *Hippopotamus*. It dates to about 116,000 - 128,000 years ago.

The periglacial deposits (blown sand and head) above the raised beach mark the encroaching cold period of the Devensian (last) glaciation. As the climate deteriorated further ice spread over the area some 18,000 years ago to deposit the Skipsea Till, which blanketed the whole sequence. Over most of Holderness the Skipsea Till rests directly on Basement Till and the Sewerby succession is thus crucial in demonstrating that the tills represent deposition during two different glacial periods. The Basement Till probably represents the Wolstonian (penultimate) glaciation, about 140,000 years ago (Catt, 1990).

Note: If the whole of the South Landing to Sewerby section is followed on a falling tide there will still not be time to return along the shore. Instead either go into Sewerby village and catch a bus back to Flamborough, or return along a footpath which follows the cliff top to Dane's Dyke and then strikes inland to Flamborough (Figure 41).

Langtoft, Foxholes and Staxton Hill

ITINERARY 14

Langtoft, Foxholes and Staxton Hill

P. F. Rawson

OS   1:25,000 Sheet TA 06/16 Langtoft, 07/17 Hunmanby
          1:50,000 Landranger 101 Scarborough
GS   1:50,000 Sheets 54 Scarborough, 64 Great Driffield

This brief itinerary links three localities along the B1249, which runs northwards across the Wolds from Driffield to Staxton. Two show inland exposures of chalk shatter zones in disused quarries immediately by the roadside, in which it is possible to park. The third, Staxton Hill, is an excellent viewpoint from which the glacial history of the Vale of Pickering area can be demonstrated. Combined with Itinerary 11 or 12 this can make a full field day, in which case drive from Flamborough to the west side of Bridlington and turn off the A165 onto the B1253 through Rudston.

Locality 1. Rudston churchyard.

The churchyard at Rudston village (TA 098678) contains the Rudston monolith, reputed to be the tallest standing stone in England. Dating to the Bronze Age, it is made of Jurassic sandstone and must have been transported for at least 16 km, possibly from the Pickering area (Allison, 1976). The grave of the East Riding's best-known novelist, Winifred Holtby, lies near the SW corner of the churchyard.

Locality 2. Langtoft (Chalk structures).

Continue westwards from Rudston to a traffic island at Octon Cross Roads where the B1253 crosses the B1249. Turn left (southwards) along the latter and drive through Langtoft. Just south of the village on the east side of the road (TA 012659) is a disused chalk quarry exposing the Flamborough Chalk Formation (probably the *rostrata* Zone). Here the chalk at the southern end of the section is almost horizontal, but northwards it is dragged up to dip of about 50°, before passing into a zone of brecciated, calcite-veined and slickenlined chalk beneath the grassy slopes at the northern end of the quarry. Note that in a quarry across the dale from here the chalk is almost horizontal, but listric shears occur, dipping 45-70° WSW (Starmer, 1995a). Starmer has suggested that this 'shatter zone' probably reflects post-alpine extensional reactivation of the E-W trending Langtoft Fault, which can traced beneath the Chalk eastwards along the northern side of Bridlington and into the offshore area (Kirby & Swallow, 1987).

Locality 3. Foxholes (Chalk structures).

From Langtoft head northwards to Foxholes. About half a kilometre north of the village on the east side of the road (TA 012735) turn into another old quarry which exposes flinty chalk of the Burnham Formation. The main face shows a mass of chalk folded to dip more or less uniformly north at about 70°, whereas in the top right-hand corner of the quarry, above the grassed-over talus slopes, the chalk is almost horizontal. The faulted contact between dipping and horizontal chalks is now difficult to see, but horizontal slickensides are sometimes visible. Vein calcite crystals can be picked up on the slopes beneath. Starmer (1995a) has shown that the folding represents compression of probable Alpine age, while the fault marks a later tensional phase. This 'shatter zone' again appears to lie over a pre-Chalk fault and extends eastwards to merge with the Bempton Fault Zone on the coast at Staple Nook (illustrated in Starmer, 1995b).

Locality 4. Staxton Hill (viewpoint; glacial features).

Continue northward to the top of Staxton Hill (TA 009778) and park at the picnic area and viewpoint (signposted). There are public toilets here, and tables in the picnic area. On a clear day there is a spectacular view of virtually the whole Vale of Pickering. In the foreground the scarp edge is formed of chalk underlain by the Hunstanton Formation and Speeton Clay, while much of the Vale is floored by Kimmeridge Clay. The dip slope of the Tabular Hills rises away from the observer in the distance (Figure 48). But the main reason for stopping here is to consider the late-glacial history and imagine the time when one would have been looking out from snow-capped hills over an extensive glacial lake. The Geologists' Association visited here on 3 August 1967, when Dr L. F. Penny gave a succinct account of the Devensian to Recent evolution of the area (Penny & Rawson, 1969, p. 204); we are grateful to Dr Penny for allowing us to reproduce it in slightly modified form here:

The Wykeham moraine, which curved half-way across the Vale of Pickering, marked the limit of an ice lobe which had entered the valley from the east. The other end of the valley was simultaneously blocked by Vale of York ice at the Ampleforth moraine. Lake Pickering extended between the two, depositing lake clays which have been proved in numerous boreholes. The lake was fed principally by the waters of the Newtondale spillway which deposited the delta on which Pickering stands; and also by those of the Forge Valley spillway which, hemmed in between the ice of the Wykeham lobe and the Corallian dip-slope, were forced westward, depositing the Hutton Buscel kame terrace and the delta fan which spread south-westward from the point where it entered the lake.

As the ice retreated from the Wykeham moraine, the waters of the Forge Valley were able to flow straight into the lake, initiating the present course of the Derwent and destroying the southern half of the Wykeham moraine (which probably abutted on the Chalk scarp around Ganton). Retreating still farther, the ice uncovered the Seamer-Scarborough Valley, whose waters then similarly flowed into the lake and deposited the Seamer delta. The position of the ice front farther south-east at this time is uncertain, but it is probably related to the Flamborough moraine, for an ice margin drawn in this way encloses an area of markedly fresher glacial topography,

Langtoft, Foxholes and Staxton Hill

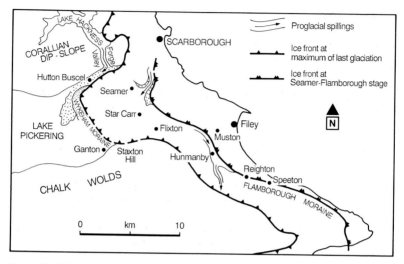

Figure 48. Glaciology of the eastern end of the Vale of Pickering.
(Redrawn from Penny& Rawson, 1969, fig. 3, by permission of the authors and
the Geologists' Association).

which includes the hummocky ground between Muston and Hunmanby and the
well-developed drumlins near Reighton. All these events relate to a period at, and
immediately after, the maximum of the Last Glaciation, but 'Lake Pickering'
probably remained in a diminished form and at a lower level until the Kirkham
spillway had been finally cut down to its present level. Certainly there was a lake
here in early post-Glacial times, the shores of which were inhabited by
Mesolithic man around Flixton and Starr Carr. The valley was still fen in historical
times, of which the many 'carrs' (fens) and 'ings' (water meadows) bear witness
throughout the area, and is still liable to severe flooding, despite the cutting of the
Hertford River and the canalisation of the Derwent in the eighteenth and nineteenth
centuries.

FURTHER READING

AGAR, R. 1960. Post-glacial erosion of the north Yorkshire coast from the Tees estuary to the Humber. *Proceedings of the Yorkshire Geological Society*, **32**, 409-428.

ALEXANDER, J. 1986. Idealised flow models to predict alluvial sandstone body distribution in the Middle Jurassic Yorkshire Basin. *Marine and Petroleum Geology*, **3**, 298-305.

ALLISON, K.J. 1976. *The East Riding of Yorkshire Landscape*. Hodder & Stoughton, 272 pp.

BATE, R.H. 1959. The Yons Nab Beds of the Middle Jurassic of the Yorkshire Coast. *Proceedings of the Yorkshire Geological Society*, **32**, 153-164.

BISAT, W.S., PENNY, L.F. & NEALE, J.W., 1962. *Geology around the University Towns: Hull*. Geologists' Association Guide No. **11**, 34 pp.

BLACK, M. 1928. 'Washouts' in the Estuarine Series of Yorkshire. *Geological Magazine*, **65**, 301-307.

BLACK, M., HEMINGWAY, J.E. & WILSON, V. 1934. Summer field meeting in N.E. Yorkshire: report by the directors. *Proceedings of the Geologists' Association*, **45**, 291-306.

BRAY, R.J., GREEN, P.F. & DUDDY, I.R. 1992. Thermal history reconstruction using apatite fission track analysis and vitrinite reflectance; a case study from the U.K. East Midlands and Southern North Sea. *Geological Society Special Publication*, **67**, 3-25.

BUCKMAN, S.S., 1915. A palaeontological classification of the Jurassic rocks of the Whitby district, with a zonal table of Liassic ammonites. Pp. 59-102 in Fox-Strangways & Barrow, *q.v.*

CATT, J.A. 1990. Geology and Relief. In (Ellis, S. & Crowther, D.R.; eds). *Humber perspectives*. Hull University Press, 13-28.

CATT, J.A. & PENNY, L.F. 1966. The Pleistocene deposits of Holderness, East Yorkshire. *Proceedings of the Yorkshire Geological Society*, **35**, 375-420.

COE, A.L., 1996. A comparison of the Oxfordian sucessions of Dorset, Oxfordshire and Yorkshire. In (Taylor, P.D.; ed.) *Field Geology of the British Jurassic*. Geological Society, London, 151-172.

DEAN, W.T. 1954. Notes on part of the Upper Lias succession at Blea Wyke,

Further Reading

Yorkshire. *Proceedings of the Yorkshire Geological Society*, **29**, 161-179.

DELAIR, J.B. & SARGEANT, W.A.S. 1985. History and bibliography of the study of fossil vertebrate footprints in the British Isles: Supplement 1973-83. *Palaeogeography, Palaeoclimatology, Palaeoecology*, **19**, 123-160.

DONATO, J.A. 1993. A buried granite batholith and the origin of the Sole Pit Basin, UK Southern North Sea. *Journal of the Geological Society, London*, **150**, 255-258.

FOX-STRANGWAYS, C. 1892. The Jurassic rocks of Great Britain, vol. 1, Yorkshire. *Memoirs of the Geological Survey of Great Britain*, lx + 551 pp.

FOX-STRANGWAYS, C. & BARROW, G. 1915. The Geology of the country between Whitby and Scarborough. *Memoirs of the Geological Survey of Great Britain* iv + 144 pp.

GODFREY, A & LASSEY, P.J. 1974. *Shipwrecks of the Yorkshire Coast.* Dalesman Books, 168 pp.

GOWLAND, S. & RIDING, J.B. 1991. Stratigraphy, sedimentology and palaeontology of the Scarborough Formation (Middle Jurassic) of Hundale Point, North Yorkshire. *Proceedings of the Yorkshire Geological Society*, **48**, 375-392.

GREENSMITH, J.T., RAWSON, P.F. & SHALABY, S.E. 1980. An association of minor fining-upwards cycles and aligned gutter marks in the Middle Lias (Lower Jurassic) of the Yorkshire Coast. *Proceedings of the Yorkshire Geological Society*, **42**, 525-538.

GREGORY, K.J. 1962. The deglaciation of eastern Eskdale, Yorkshire. *Proceedings of the Yorkshire Geological Society*, **33**, 363-380.

GREGORY, K.J. 1965. Proglacial Lake Eskdale after 60 years. *Transactions of the Institute of British Geographers*, **36**, 149-161. '

HARRIS, T.M., 1953. The Geology of the Yorkshire flora. *Proceedings of the Yorkshire Geological Society*, **29**, 63-71.

HEMINGWAY, J.E. 1953. Report of a field meeting at Whitby. *Proceedings of the Yorkshire Geological Society*, **28**, 118-122.

HEMINGWAY, J.E. 1974. Jurassic. In (Rayner, D.H. & Hemingway, J.E.; eds) *The Geology and Mineral Resources of Yorkshire*. Leeds (Yorkshire Geological Society), 161-223.

HEMINGWAY, J.E. & RIDDLER, G.P. 1982. Basin inversion in North Yorkshire.

Further Reading

Transactions of the Institute of Mining and Metallurgy (section B), **91**, B175-B186.

HEMINGWAY, J.E., WILSON, V & WRIGHT, C.W. 1968. *Geology of the Yorkshire Coast.* Geol. Ass. Guide No. **34**, 47 pp. (revised edition).

HERBIN, J.-P., MULLER, C., GEYSSANT, J.R., MÉLIÈRES, F. & PENN, I.E. 1991. Hétérogénéité quantitative et qualitative de la matière organique dans les argiles du Kimmeridgien du Val de Pickering (Yorkshire, UK). *Revue de l'Institut Français du Pétrole,* **46**, 675-712.

HESSELBO, S.P. & JENKYNS, H.C., 1996. A comparison of the Hettangian to Bajocian successions of Dorset and Yorkshire. In (Taylor, P.D.; ed.) *Field geology of the British Jurassic.* Geological Society, London, 105-150.

HOWARD, A.S. 1985. Lithostratigraphy of the Staithes Sandstone and Cleveland Ironstone Formations (Lower Jurassic) of north-east Yorkshire. *Proceedings of the Yorkshire Geological Society,* **45**, 261-275.

HOWARTH, M.K. 1955. Domerian of the Yorkshire Coast. *Proceedings of the Yorkshire Geological Society,* **30**, 147-175.

HOWARTH, M.K. 1962. The Jet Rock Series and the Alum Shale Series of the Yorkshire Coast. *Proceedings of the Yorkshire Geological Society,* **33**, 381-422.

HOWARTH, M.K. 1973. The stratigraphy and ammonite fauna of the Upper Liassic Grey Shales of the Yorkshire Coast. *Bulletin of the British Museum (Natural History), Geology,* **24**, 235-277.

HUDLESTON, W.H. 1878. The Yorkshire oolites, Pt 2, the Middle Oolites. Section 2, the Coralline Oolites, Coral Rag and Supra-Coralline Beds. *Proceedings of the Geologists' Association,* **5**, 407-494.

IVENS, C.R. & WATSON, G.G. 1994. *Records of dinosaur footprints on the North East Yorkshire Coast.* Roseberry Publications, Middlesborough. 20 pp.

JACKSON, J.W. 1911. A new species of *Unio* from the Yorkshire Estuarine Series. *The Naturalist, 1911,* 211-214.

JEANS, C.V. 1980. Early submarine lithification in the Red Chalk and Lower Chalk of Eastern England: a bacterial control model and its implications. *Proceedings of the Yorkshire Geological Society,* **43**, 81-157.

KANTOROWICZ, J.D. 1990. Lateral and vertical variation in pedogenesis and other early diagenetic phenomena, Middle Jurassic Ravenscar Group, Yorkshire. *Proceedings of the Yorkshire Geological Society* **48**, 61-74.

Further Reading

KENDALL, P.F. 1902. A system of glacier lakes in the Cleveland Hills. *Quarterly Journal of the Geological Society of London*, **58**, 471-571.

KENT, P.E. 1980a. Subsidence and uplift in East Yorkshire and Lincolnshire: a double inversion. *Proceedings of the Yorkshire Geological Society*, **42**, 505-524.

KENT. P.E. 1980b. *Eastern England from the Tees to the Wash.* British Regional Geology, HMSO, vii + 155 pp.

KIRBY, G.A. & SWALLOW, P.W. 1987. Tectonism and sedimentation in the Flamborough Head region of north-east England. *Proceedings of the Yorkshire Geological Society*, **46**, 301-309.

KNOX, R.W.O'B. 1973. The Eller Beck Bed (Bajocian) of the Ravenscar Group of north-east Yorkshire. *Geological Magazine*, **110**, 511-534.

KNOX, R.W.O'B. 1984. Lithostratigraphy and depositional history of the late Toarcian sequence at Ravenscar, Yorkshire. *Proceedings of the Yorkshire Geological Society*, **45**, 99-108.

KNOX, R.W.O'B. 1991. Ryazanian to Barremian mineral stratigraphy of the Speeton Clay in the southern North Sea Basin. *Proceedings of the Yorkshire Geological Society*, **48**, 255-264.

KNOX, R.W.O'B, HOWARD, A.S., POWELL, J.H. & VAN BUCHEM, F. 1991. Lower and Middle Jurassic sediments of the Cleveland Basin, N.E. England: shallow marine and paralic facies seen in their sequence stratigraphic context. *13th International Sedimentological Congress, Field Guide No. 5.*

KONIJNENBURG-van CITTERN, J. H. A. van & MORGANS, H. S. 1999. *The Jurassic Flora of Yorkshire.* Palaeontological Association field guide to fossils, no. **8**, 134 pp.

LAMPLUGH, G.W. 1889. On the subdivisions of the Speeton Clay. *Quarterly Journal of the Geological Society of London*, **45**, 575-618.

LAMPLUGH, G.W. 1896. Notes on the White Chalk of Yorkshire. Part III. The Geology of Flamborough Head, with notes on the Yorkshire Wolds. *Proceedings of the Yorkshire Geological Society*, **13**, 171-191.

LINTON, D.L. 1955. The problem of Tors. *Geographical Journal*, **121**, 470-487.

LIVERA, S.E. & LEEDER, M.R. 1981. The Middle Jurassic Ravenscar Group ('Deltaic Series') of Yorkshire: recent sedimentological studies as demonstrated during a field meeting, 2-3 May 1980. *Proceedings of the Geologists' Association*, **92**, 241-250.

Further Reading

MIDDLEMISS, F.A. 1976. Lower Cretaceous Terebratulinida of Northern England and Germany and their geological background. *Geologisches Jahrbuch* **A30**, 21-104.

MILSOM, J. & RAWSON, P.F. 1989. The Peak Trough - a major control on the geology of the North Yorkshire coast. *Geological Magazine*, **126**, 699-705.

MITCHELL, S.F. 1994. New data on the biostratigraphy of the Flamborough Chalk Formation (Santonian, Upper Cretaceous) between South Landing and Danes Dyke, North Yorkshire. *Proceedings of the Yorkshire Geological Society*, **50**, 113-118.

MITCHELL, S.F. 1995. Lithostratigraphy and biostratigraphy of the Hunstanton Formation (Red Chalk, Cretaceous) succession at Speeton, North Yorkshire, England. *Proceedings of the Yorkshire Geological Society*, **50**, 285-303.

MORRIS, K.A. 1979. A classification of Jurassic marine shale sequences: an example from the Toarcian (Lower Jurassic) of Great Britain. *Palaeogeography, Palaeoclimatology, Palaeoecology*, **26**, 117-126.

NAMI, M. 1976. An exhumed Jurassic meander belt from Yorkshire. *Geological Magazine*, **113**, 47-52.

NAMI, M. & LEEDER, M.R. 1978. Changing channel morphologies and magnitude in the Scalby Formation (Middle Jurassic) of Yorkshire (England). In (Miall, A.D.; Ed.) *Fluvial sedimentation*. Canadian Society of Petroleum Geologists, Memoir, **5**, 431-440.

OSBORNE, R. 1998. *The Floating Egg*. Jonathan Cape, London, xii + 372 pp.

OWEN, J.S. 1985. *Staithes and Port Mulgrave Ironstone*. The Cleveland Industrial Archaeological Research Report no. **4**, 41 pp.

PAGE, K.N. 1989. A stratigraphic revision for the English Lower Callovian. *Proceedings of the Geologists' Association*, **100**, 363-382.

PALMER, J. 1956. Tor formation at the Bridestones in North-east Yorkshire, and its significance in relation to problems of valley-side development and regional glaciation. *Transactions of the Institute of British Geographers*, **22**, 55-72.

PARSONS, C.F. 1977. A stratigraphical revision of the Scarborough Formation. *Proceedings of the Yorkshire Geological Society*, **41**, 203-222.

PARSONS, C.F. 1980. The Aalenian and Bajocial Stages. In (Cope, J.C.W. *et al.*; eds) *A correlation of the Jurassic rocks in the British Isles. Part Two: Middle and Upper Jurassic*. Geological Society of London, Special Report **15**, 3-21.

Further Reading

PENNY, L.F. & RAWSON, P.F., 1969. Field meeting in East Yorkshire and North Lincolnshire. *Proceedings of the Geologists' Association*, **80**, 193-218.

PHILLIPS, J. 1829. *Illustrations of the Geology of Yorkshire; Part 1. - the Yorkshire Coast*. London, xvi + 192 pp. (2nd edit. 1835, 3rd edit. 1875).

POWELL, J.H., 1984. Lithostratigraphic nomenclature of the Lias Group in the Yorkshire Basin. *Proceedings of the Yorkshire Geological Society*, **45**, 51-57.

PYE, K. & KRINSLEY, D.H. 1986. Microfabric, mineralogy and early diagenetic history of the Whitby Mudstone Formation (Toarcian), Cleveland Basin, U.K. *Geological Magazine*, **123**, 191-203.

RASTALL, R.H. & HEMINGWAY, J.E. 1940. The Yorkshire Dogger, 1. The coastal region. *Geological Magazine*, **77**, 177-197.

RAWSON, P.F., CURRY, D., DILLEY, F.C., HANCOCK, J.M., KENNEDY, W.J., NEALE, J.W., WOOD, C. J. & WORSSAM, B.C. 1978. *A correlation of Cretaceous rocks in the British Isles*, Geological Society of London, Special Report **9**, 70 pp.

RAWSON, P.F., GREENSMITH, J.T. & SHALABY, S.E. 1983. Coarsening upwards cycles in the uppermost Staithes and Cleveland Ironstone Formations (Lower Jurassic) of the Yorkshire coast, England. *Proceedings of the Geologists' Association*, **94**, 91-93.

RAWSON, P.F. & MUTTERLOSE, J. 1983. Stratigraphy of the Lower B and basal Cement Beds (Barremian) of the Speeton Clay, Yorkshire, England. *Proceedings of the Geologists' Association*, **94**, 133-146.

RAWSON, P.F. & RILEY, L.A. 1982. Latest Jurassic - Early Cretaceous events and the 'Late Cimmerian Unconformity' in North Sea area. *Bulletin of the American Association of Petroleum Geologists*, **66**, 2628-2648.

RAWSON, P.F. & WRIGHT, J.K. 1996. Jurassic of the Cleveland Basin, North Yorkshire. In (Taylor, P.D.; ed.) *Field Geology of the British Jurassic*. Geological Society, London, 173-208.

RIDING, J.B. 1984. A palynological investigation of Toarcian to early Aalenian strata from the Blea Wyke area, Ravenscar, North Yorkshire. *Proceedings of the Yorkshire Geological Society*, **45**, 109-122.

RIDING, J.B. & WRIGHT, J.K. 1989. Palynostratigraphy of the Scalby Formation (Middle Jurassic) of the Cleveland Basin, north-east Yorkshire. *Proceedings of the Yorkshire Geological Society*, **47**, 349-354.

Further Reading

ROWE, A.W. 1904. The zones of the White Chalk of the English coast. IV - Yorkshire. *Geological Magazine*, **99**, 273-278.

SARGEANT, W.A.S. 1970. Fossil footprints from the Middle Trias of Nottinghamshire and the Middle Jurassic of Yorkshire. *Mercian Geologist*, **3**, 269-282.

SELLWOOD, B.W. 1970. The relation of trace fossils to small-scale sedimentary cycles in the British Lias. *Geological Journal Special Issue*, **3**, 489-504.

SELLWOOD, B.W. 1972. Regional environmental change across a Lower Jurassic stage boundary in Britain. *Palaeontology*, **15**, 125-157.

SENIOR, J.R. 1994. The Lower Jurassic rocks between Staithes and Port Mulgrave. In (Scrutton, C.; ed.) *Yorkshire rocks and landscape. A field guide.* Yorkshire Geological Society, 224 pp.

STARMER, I.C. 1995a. Deformation of the Upper Cretaceous Chalk at Selwicks Bay, Flamborough Head, Yorkshire: its significance in the structural evolution of north-east England and the North Sea Basin. *Proceedings of the Yorkshire Geological Society*, **50**, 213-228.

STARMER, I.C. 1995b. Contortions in the Chalk at Staple Nook, Flamborough Head. *Proceedings of the Yorkshire Geological Society*, **50**, 271-275.

VAN BUCHEM, F.S.P. & McCAVE, I.N. 1989. Cyclic sedimentation patterns in Lower Lias mudstones of Yorkshire (Great Britain). *Terra Nova*, **1**, 461-467.

VAN BUCHEM, F.S.P., McCAVE, I.N. & WEEDON, G.P. 1994. Orbitally induced small scale cyclicity in a siliclastic epicontinental setting (Cleveland Basin, Lower Lias, Yorkshire, UK). In (De Boer, P.L. & Smith, D.G.; eds) *Orbital forcing and cyclic sedimentary sequences.* Special Publications of the International Association of Sedimentologists, **19**, 345-366.

VAN BUCHEM, F.S.P., MELNYK, D.H. & McCAVE, I.N., 1992. Chemical cyclicity and correlation of Lower Lias Mudstones using gamma ray logs, Yorkshire, UK. *Journal of the Geological Society, London*, **149**, 991-1002.

VERSEY, H.C. 1939. The Tertiary History of East Yorkshire. *Proceedings of the Yorkshire Geological Society*, **23**, 302-314.

WHITHAM, F. 1991. The stratigraphy of the Upper Cretaceous Ferriby, Welton and Burnham Formations north of the Humber, north-east England. *Proceedings of the Yorkshire Geological Society*, **48**, 227-254.

Further Reading

WHITHAM, F. 1993. The stratigraphy of the Upper Cretaceous Flamborough Chalk Formation north of the Humber, north-east England. *Proceedings of the Yorkshire Geological Society*, **49**, 235-258.

WHYTE, M.A. & ROMANO, M. 1993. Footprints of a sauropod dinosaur from the Middle Jurassic of Yorkshire. *Proceedings of the Geologists' Association,* **104**, 195-199.

WILSON, V. 1949. The lower Corallian rocks of the Yorkshire coast and Hackness Hills. *Proceedings of the Geologists' Association*, **60**, 235-271.

WOOD, C.J. & SMITH, D. 1978. Lithostratigraphic nomenclature of the Chalk in North Yorkshire, Humberside and Lincolnshire. *Proceedings of the Yorkshire Geological Society*, **42**, 263-287.

WRAY, D.S. & WOOD, C.J. 1998. Distinction between detrital and volcanogenic clay-rich beds in Turonian-Coniacian chalks of eastern England. *Proceedings of the Yorkshire Geological Society*, **52**, 95-105.

WRIGHT, J.K. 1968. The stratigraphy of the Callovian rocks between Newtondale and the Scarborough coast, Yorkshire. *Proceedings of the Geologists' Association,* **79**, 363-399.

WRIGHT, J. K. 1972. The stratigraphy of the Yorkshire Corallian. *Proceedings of the Yorkshire Geological Society*, **39**, 225-266.

WRIGHT, J.K. 1977. The Cornbrash Formation (Callovian) in North Yorkshire and Cleveland. *Proceedings of the Yorkshire Geological Society*, **41**, 325-346.

WRIGHT, J.K. 1978. The Callovian succession (excluding Cornbrash) in the western and northern parts of the Yorkshire Basin. *Proceedings of the Geologists' Association*, **89**, 239-261.

WRIGHT, J.K. 1983. The Lower Oxfordian (Upper Jurassic) of North Yorkshire. *Proceedings of the Yorkshire Geological Society*, **44**, 249-281.

WRIGHT, J.K. 1992. The depositional history of the Hackness Coral-Sponge Bed and its associated sediments within the Passage Beds Member of the Coralline Oolite Formation (Corallian Group; Oxfordian) of North Yorkshire. *Proceedings of the Yorkshire Geological Society,* **49**, 155-168.

YOUNG, G. & BIRD, J. 1822. *A Geological Survey of the Yorkshire Coast.* Clark, Whitby, iv + 322 pp. (2nd edit. 1828).

Notes

Notes